Volume 6
CULTIVATOR

DYNAMOMETER

The ILLUSTRATED
SCIENCE *and* INVENTION
ENCYCLOPEDIA

International Edition

H. S. STUTTMAN CO., INC. *publishers*   New York, N.Y. 10016

how it works

Published by H. S. STUTTMAN CO., Inc.
New York, N.Y. 10016
© Marshall Cavendish Limited 1974, 1976, 1977

CULTIVATOR

Before World War 1 farmers practised cultivation by drawing a steel chisel or *tine* (similar to the prongs of a fork) through the upturned furrows of ploughed land to work the soil down to a soft powdery consistency in which seeds could be successfully sown.

Nowadays powered cultivation is widely used not only to work down ploughed and fallow ground into seed bed condition, but often to replace the task of first ploughing the land. The machines used for this job are called *rotary cultivators* because they work basically by a series of revolving blades chopping up the land. The first prototype machine was produced in Australia in 1912 by A C Howard (1896-1971), but his first really successful tractor powered machine was not built until 1922. This was a large machine with a 15 ft (4.5 m) working width, much larger than the models which were subsequently to become commercially viable.

Rotary cultivator   Most rotary cultivators work on the principle of cutting the soil by means of L-shaped or curved hoe blades bolted to a robust central axle, which is either driven by the machine's own engine or by the power take-off drive shaft on the tractor on which the cultivator is mounted.

Because these machines have to suffer heavy punishment in work, the strongest steels are used in the manufacture of the blades, which rarely break even though they frequently strike large stones in the soil with great force. The blades are usually mounted on the central shaft in spiralling order so that the shock loading on the tractor transmission is evened out as much as possible.

Small pedestrian controlled rotary cultivators are very popular nowadays with horticulturists, market gardeners, and even allotment holders. The principle is the same as for the larger agricultural models—an overmounted engine drives a rotor armed with hoe blades that strike into the soil to leave a well-worked seed bed in its wake. Such machines usually have a power of 10 hp and a working width of under 1 yard (1 m).

Tractor mounted or hand controlled rotary cultivators are rarely used to dig deeper than 8 in (20 cm), as seeds are never sown as deeply as this. Ideally a seed bed should have deep soil fractures that break down into small lumps below the surface, reducing to even smaller friable lumps and free soil on the top. By varying the rotor speed with the rate of forward travel, a farmer is able to get the degree of coarseness into his *tilth* or seed bed that he requires. Another advantage of the rotary cultivator is that it will chop unwanted crop residues into a *mulch* (mixture of stalk, leaves and straw) or compost of decomposing vegetation which will manure the ensuing crop.

Modified cultivators   A modern trend has been to combine the seeding and drilling machine (for drilling seed holes) with the tractor drawn variety of rotary cultivator. In this way the farmer is saved making a second journey over the ground drilling the seed. The drill, which is usually fixed above the cultivator hood, feeds its seeds into the freshly prepared earth via spouts which discharge just behind the rotating hoe blades. A further time and labour saving improvement that has been made is to split the drill's hopper into two compartments, one holding seed and the other

The spike rotor cultivator is an alternative to the standard rotor and L-shaped blades. It is ideal for producing deep tilth seedbeds or for shallow cultivation, and because it takes much less power than the standard rotor with blades, works at 4 to 5 mph (6 to 8 km/h), and can cultivate up to 40 acres (16 ha) in a day.

HOWARD ROTAVATOR

APIS

holding artificial fertilizer.

Naturally a machine that performs three separate functions while making one pass over the ground must be accurately calibrated to deliver the correct amounts of seed and fertilizer into land that the machine has adequately prepared for sowing, or the whole benefit from combining two or more jobs will be lost. Jobs that are combined in this way are described by farmers as a *minimum tillage (cultivation) system*.

One machine for achieving this, an Italian design, is a tractor drawn giant rotary cultivator which is powered by its own 315 hp diesel engine. It is 12 ft (3.6 m) wide and capable of performing seven tasks. These include burying trash, cultivating the seed bed, applying pesticides, sowing seeds, applying fertilizer, covering and firming seeds, and finally applying weedkiller.

These tasks are normally undertaken separately, but with this type of machine farmers could hire one to come and do all the field work needed for the year in an afternoon.

Above: the machine above must surely be classed as the king of all minimum cultivation systems; it is called the 'supercoltivatrice'. Made in Italy, it is essentially a trailed supersized rotary cultivator. In a single run over the soil it will chop the residue of a previous crop, such as maize (corn) and simultaneously prepare the ground to receive the next crop. It goes one better than sowing broadcast (scattered) seed, as one might for cereal harvests. This Italian giant can precision-sow rows of crops, such as maize, that need one seed every four inches (10 cm) apart, and will also add the chemical fertilizers. In addition this machine applies pesticides to the soil, and a following assemblage of placement rollers covers the seed out of sight of birds. Finally a spray of pre-emergent weedkiller guarantees that the soil will not grow any weeds before the maize crop seedlings break the surface. In many cases no further field work is needed before the crop is harvested.

Above right: a tractor drawn general purpose cultivator used for stubble cleaning (churning up weeds), preparing seed beds and so on.

MASSEY FERGUSON

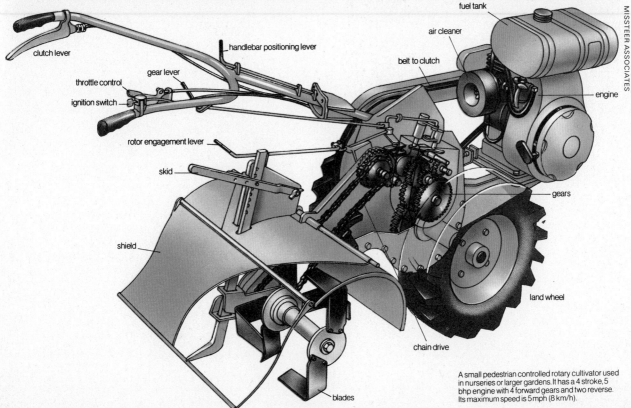

MISSTEER ASSOCIATES

fuel tank

air cleaner

belt to clutch

engine

clutch lever

handlebar positioning lever

gear lever

throttle control

ignition switch

rotor engagement lever

skid

shield

gears

chain drive

land wheel

blades

A small pedestrian controlled rotary cultivator used in nurseries or larger gardens. It has a 4 stroke, 5 bhp engine with 4 forward gears and two reverse. Its maximum speed is 5 mph (8 km/h).

CURIE, P(1859-1906) & M (1867-1934)

Marie and Pierre Curie, one of the greatest husband and wife teams in the history of science, made fundamental discoveries about the RADIOACTIVITY of ATOMS, and discovered the radioactive elements polonium (Po) and radium (Ra).

Pierre Curie was born in Paris, France, the son of a physician. He was not a rapid learner, having something of the dreamer in him, but he took readily to mathematics and was particularly at home with geometry. He later applied this talent to the study of the geometrical forms in CRYSTALS.

Pierre became a physics teacher in Paris at the age of 19. He collaborated with his elder brother Jacques on studies of crystals, which culminated in 1880 with the discovery of PIEZOELECTRICITY. This is the production of an electric charge by pressure on certain crystals, a principle which is now used in MICROPHONES and ceramic record player pickups.

Pierre became director of laboratory work at the School of Industrial Physics and Chemistry in Paris, where he worked for the next 22 years. Here, he extended his researches on crystals, and deduced from them one of the underlying principles of modern science, that there is an underlying symmetry to the physical world.

Because Pierre had no laboratory of his own at the school, he had to set up his experiments in a corridor outside a classroom. Starting in 1891, he began the studies on magnetism that led to his doctor's thesis. He discovered the *Curie point,* a temperature at which ferromagnetic substances lose their magnetism.

He presented his thesis in 1895. Although he was shy and reserved, and not one to press for his own advancement, he was promoted to a professorship in belated recognition of his scientific ability. The previous year, he had met a Polish girl student named Marie Sklodovska. She had left her native Warsaw in 1891 to study at the Sorbonne, and lived, penniless, in a tiny room, fainting on one occasion from hunger in class. But she graduated at the top of her year.

Pierre Curie had devoted his life to science, and could only have married a brilliant woman of similar interests. In his letters to Marie, Pierre spoke of 'our dream for humanity, our dream for science'. They were to form the closest of personal and scientific partnerships.

After their marriage in 1895, Marie began to work with Pierre. In 1897 she decided to investigate the strange rays that Henri BECQUEREL had discovered coming from URANIUM. She found that the amount of radiation depended on the amount of uranium in the sample, and discovered that thorium compounds emit similar rays to uranium. Marie termed this effect 'radioactivity'.

But she found that some ores gave out more radioactivity than could be explained by the presence of uranium and thorium. She realized that traces of a new radioactive element must exist in these ores. Pierre laid aside his own researches to help in the study of pitchblende, a mineral with four times as much radioactivity as uranium oxide.

They found that radioactivity occurred in two chemically separate parts of the pitchblende, showing that there were

Top right: Pierre and Marie Curie in the early 1900s.

Right: pitchblende contains between 50 and 80% uranium oxide, but because of its high radioactivity the Curies postulated the existence of a new radioactive element. In the centre of this sample is a fresh plain fracture of the pitchblende crystals.

ULLSTEIN

FOTO: HANSMANN/MÜNCHEN

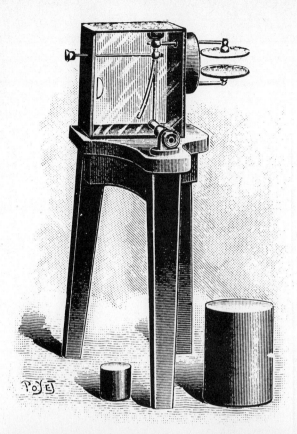

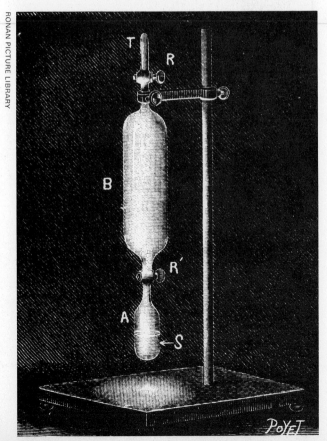

two new radioactive elements to be found. One of them had properties similar to bismuth. Marie named this polonium, after her native land. The other, even more radioactive, was hard to separate from barium. She called it radium. The Curies announced these new elements in July and December 1898 respectively.

But they had to produce pure samples to study. Working in a poorly heated wooden shed with a leaky glass roof, Marie Curie began to boil down tons of pitchblende to find usable amounts of the new elements. Even in the worst weather they had to work with the windows open to let out the choking fumes. They often ate as they worked, and drank tea to warm themselves. Marie wrote afterwards that they were pre-occupied, as in a dream. If they returned at night to continue the work, they saw the radium samples glowing with a green colour from the shelves.

By 1902, Marie had produced 0.1 grammes of radium chloride from over a ton of pitchblende. It took another eight years before she had grains of pure radium in her hand. The Curies published their results openly, with no attempt to patent their process or profit from it in any way. 'We were working in the interests of science', Marie later explained.

They became international celebrities for their discoveries, which revolutionized the understanding of atomic structure, and introduced the new technique of radiation therapy into medicine. In 1903, Henri Becquerel and the Curies shared the physics Nobel prize for their work on radioactivity.

But tragedy was soon to mar their finest hour. Pierre died instantly when hit by a wagon in a Paris street in 1906. Marie, although with two daughters to raise, continued her work. She was appointed to Pierre's professorship, and a special institute was set up for her to continue her work. In 1911 she won her second Nobel prize, in chemistry this time, for the discovery and study of radium. But she also accepted it posthumously on behalf of Pierre.

Marie's first daughter, Irène, joined her mother to work in the Radium Institute. In 1926 she married Frédéric Joliot, one of her mother's assistants. Under the combined name Joliot-Curie, they were to continue the work of the Curies, winning a Nobel prize of their own in 1935, for the discovery of artificial radioactivity.

With advancing years, Marie Curie's health began to fail. Her hands had been damaged by exposure to radioactive substances. Although by then the dangers of radium were known, she ignored the health hazards. By 1933, it was clear that she was dying from the physical damage of continued exposure to radiation. On 4 July, 1934, she died of leukemia. The same disease later claimed her daughter Irène.

CURRENT, ELECTRIC (see circuit, electric)

Top left: apparatus used by the Curies for detecting the presence of radioactivity. It consists of a gold leaf electroscope fitted with a microscope to detect the smallest movement of the leaf. The radiation emitted from radium, for example, consists of alpha and beta particles and gamma rays travelling at very high speeds which leave ionized atoms in their wake. A radium sample held near the electrodes of the detector causes charges to be accumulated on the leaf which moves through electrostatic repulsion.

Left: apparatus used by the Curies for studying the glow of substances (in B) caused by a radium salt solution (S).

CUTLERY manufacture

Knives were one of man's earliest tools, second only in importance to the axe. Originally they were made of stone—usually flint—and, despite the skill needed to fashion this material, it is probable that each man was his own cutler and made his own knives as necessary.

The first metal knives were of copper, soon superseded by bronze. Some Bronze Age knives were remarkably similar to modern ones, having a blade, bolster and a tang to which a non-metallic handle was fitted. (The bolster is the thick knob-like section against which the handle abuts.)

The advent of iron did not particularly enhance the quality of knives, but being more abundant it enabled cheaper knives to be made. The real breakthrough came with the discovery that iron could be converted into steel by heating it in a bed of charcoal so that carbon from the latter diffused into the iron to produce an alloy which could be hardened by heating and quenching in water (see HEAT TREATMENT). Although methods of making steel changed considerably, knives continued to be made from ordinary steel until 1913 when a Sheffield metallurgist, Harry Brearley, discovered that the addition of 12% or more chromium produced a steel that did not rust—stainless steel.

Mediaeval table knives were generally pointed, to enable meat to be speared for transfer to the mouth. It was not until the introduction of table forks in the seventeenth century that English knives acquired their typically rounded tips.

Spoons of stone, clay and probably wood were used in prehistoric times. By Roman times, dainty spoons that would not be out of place on a modern table had been developed. Early table forks had two prongs (tines), and were no doubt miniature versions of carving forks. By the end of the seventeenth century, three and four tined forks were in use. During Victorian times, four tined forks became standard, although five and even six tined forks were also made. Because spoons and forks are not required to be as hard as knives, a wider variety of metals had been used including gold, silver, brass, bronze and pewter.

In Europe, the utilization of water power to operate forge

Below: a sequence of drawings which illustrate the basic steps in the manufacture of cutlery. Some of the polishing is done with strips of cloth, which can polish between the tines of the fork. If cutlery is made entirely of stainless steel, electro-plating is unnecessary. Some table knives are made with hollow handles, in which case the handles are made in two halves and the finished knife must be welded, brazed or cemented together.

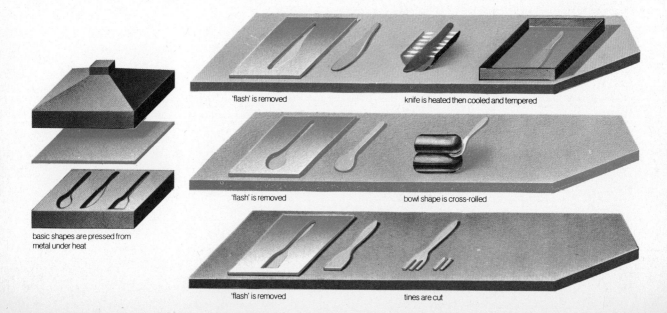

basic shapes are pressed from metal under heat

'flash' is removed

knife is heated then cooled and tempered

'flash' is removed

bowl shape is cross-rolled

'flash' is removed

tines are cut

Far left: the first stage in knife manufacture is the pre-heating of lengths of steel to about 1150°C (2102°F) so that they are soft enough to be formed roughly into shape by a press. Spoons and forks are usually made from a softer metal than knives and the billets do not need heating.

Left: a press for stamping pre-heated steel billets into rough knife shapes.

Above left: the rough shape of a knife formed by stamping a heated steel billet between two hard steel dies in a power press.

Above centre: smoothing the tines of a fork on an abrasive wheel.

Above right: polishing sterling silver spoons. A high degree of polish can be achieved using machines like this.

hammers and grinding wheels during the Middle Ages produced an early development of the cutlery industry. This is why today most European cutlery manufacture is concentrated in hilly towns with fast flowing rivers; typical examples are Sheffield in England, Solingen in Germany and Thiers in the Massif Central of France.

Knife manufacture Modern table knife blades are normally made from stainless steel containing from 12% to 16% chromium, which imparts corrosion resistance, and up to 0.5% carbon to make the steel hard when subjected to heat treatment. Knives are usually formed from short lengths of steel bar at high temperature, about 1150°C (2102°F). The heated steel is placed between two hardened steel dies which are forced together in a drop hammer or powerful press so that the steel acquires the shape of the impressions in the dies. The entire knife can be shaped in this way, but sometimes the blade is only partially formed at this stage and is hot rolled to its final thickness as a second operation. After excess metal (flash) has been trimmed from the edges of the forging, the blade is hardened by heating it to 1040°C (1904°F) and cooling it between clamps to keep it straight. Tempering, a slow low temperature treatment which eliminates brittleness, is next applied to toughen the blade.

One piece knives will have their handles formed at the same time as the blade, but for other types of knife the forging consists of a blade, bolster and round or oval shaped tang to which a separate handle is subsequently fitted. To remove scale (oxides formed during heating) and to achieve a uniformly contoured surface, the blade is ground, one side at a time. Machines are used which manipulate the blade against a grinding wheel in such a way that a thin edge of uniform thickness is achieved, while at the same time producing a blade back which is thickest near the handle where stresses in use are greatest.

Next follows a series of abrasive operations until all surfaces are finally polished. Various parts of the knife are presented in turn to rotating wheels of leather, canvas or felt and dressed with a variety of progressively finer abrasives. For most of these operations, machines are used which are

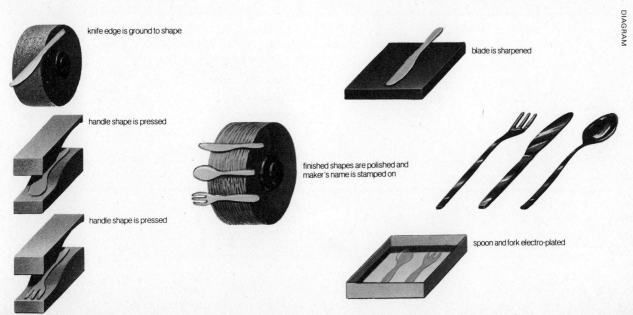

knife edge is ground to shape

blade is sharpened

handle shape is pressed

handle shape is pressed

finished shapes are polished and maker's name is stamped on

spoon and fork electro-plated

designed to manipulate the knives against the wheels—in some cases as many as thirty or forty knives are polished simultaneously.

Plastic handles are usually injection moulded. They contain a hole somewhat smaller than the blade tang over which the handle is forced. Other non-metal handles may be of wood, stag horn, porcelain or wood laminates consolidated with plastic under heat and pressure. They have holes appreciably larger than the blade tangs and are fixed with strong adhesives or cements. Many high quality carving knives have flat tangs with holes in them; the two handle-halves are riveted together with the tang between.

Some metal handles are hollow and made of stainless steel or are of silver plated nickel-silver—a copper-zinc-nickel alloy—or even sterling silver. Thin rectangular pieces of the metal are cold formed between two dies in a press or drop hammer to produce shell-like handle halves. When two such pieces are welded or brazed together they form the complete handle. Hollow handles of stainless steel are usually attached to the blade by welding. Silver handles are attached by a magnesia cement; nickel-silver handles are either cemented or brazed onto the bolster.

After whetting or sharpening the edge by grinding at an acute angle on a fine wheel, the side of the blade is marked with the maker's name; the wide variety of marking methods used includes acid etching and ELECTROCHEMICAL MACHINING.

Spoon and fork manufacture
Most spoons and forks are either silver plated or are made of stainless steel throughout. Stainless steels used for spoons and forks do not need to be particularly hard—hence they contain virtually no carbon and can have as much as 18% chromium with (for the more expensive types) from 8% to 10% nickel to enhance corrosion resistance. These steels cannot be hardened by heat treatment.

Beneath the coating of silver plated spoons and forks, the base metal is usually nickel-silver, but in recent years the high cost of copper has influenced some manufacturers to adopt stainless steel as the base metal for silver plate. A limited number of spoons and forks are made entirely of sterling silver, which by law must contain at least 92.5% silver.

Some lower priced articles are chromium plated over a base metal of mild steel, a non-stainless steel containing very little carbon, which is subsequently electroplated with copper followed by a thicker deposit of nickel as protection against rust before the final coating of chromium is applied.

Spoon and fork manufacture differs from that of knives in that it is not necessary to heat the metal to form it: the metals used can be deformed with less effort than the harder stainless steel used for knives, and in any case the shape is more easily achieved.

Whatever metal is used, manufacturing methods are virtually the same. Sheets of metal, about 0.1 inches (2.5 mm) thick if intended for dessert spoons or forks, are cut into strips from which shapes similar in outline to that of a fork are blanked out. The end intended to form the spoon bowl is then cross rolled—passed sideways several times between the ends of heavy steel rolls to increase its width and reduce its thickness to about half that of the handle. In the case of forks, cross rolling is rarely applied and then only lightly because it is not essential for tines to be thinner than the handle. The tines themselves are formed by cutting out longitudinal slots between shaped tools in a press.

If particularly deep bowls are to be formed, it is necessary at this stage to carry out a heat treatment known as annealing in order to reduce the hardness created by cold rolling. To avoid the formation of scale this annealing is carried out in a special atmosphere, for example a mixture of hydrogen and nitrogen, so that the surfaces remain bright. Stainless steel is annealed by heating to 1050°C (1922°F) whereas nickel-silver is heated to about 700°C (1292°F).

The final shape is achieved by placing the partly formed piece between two steel dies. The surfaces of the dies are particularly smooth so that they do not roughen the surface of the spoon or fork and make subsequent polishing operations more difficult.

Edges of the spoons and forks are polished first, generally on a series of abrasive belts of progressively finer grits. Abrasive belts are also used to polish between the prongs of forks. The main surfaces of the articles are polished in automatic machines which manipulate two or three dozen at once between rotating polishing rolls. These rolls are made of soft materials such as calico so that they can conform to the shape of the spoons and forks. Fine abrasive mixed in oil is sprayed on the polishing rolls.

In the case of plated spoons and forks, electroplating is carried out before final polishing. After the articles have been well cleaned in organic solvents they are attached to metal racks or hung on wires which in turn can be connected to the negative terminal of a direct current supply of electricity. Before the actual plating takes place, the pieces are subjected to a series of pretreatments to ensure that all foreign matter is removed so that the metal deposit will adhere. They are then placed in the plating bath, which contains an electrolyte. Anodes made of the metal to be deposited are also suspended in the electrolyte and connected to the positive terminal of the direct current supply. The amount of metal transferred from the anodes to the spoons and forks is directly proportional to the current flowing and to the duration of plating. It is a simple matter therefore to deposit a known weight of metal, but considerable skill is needed to ensure that it is uniformly distributed.

Silver deposits used to be quoted in pennyweights per dozen articles, but the modern and more readily understood method is to quote the average thickness in micrometres (millionths of a metre, or microns). Good quality cutlery is likely to have a silver thickness of 20 micrometres and it may be as much as 35 micrometres.

CYCLOTRON (see particle accelerator)

DACRON (see fibre, synthetic)

After stamping, the knives go through several finishing processes to remove excess metal and to sharpen and polish them.

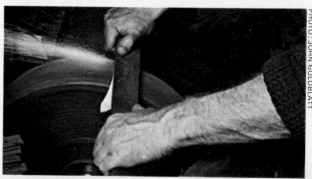

DAGUERRE, L J M (1787-1851)

Louis Jacques Mandé Daguerre, the inventor of the first workable photographic process, was born at Cormeilles-en-Parisis on 18 November 1787, the son of a magistrate's court official. He showed early talent for drawing, and at the age of 16 began studying under the designer at the Paris Opera. Three years later he became the assistant of the panorama painter, Pierre Prevost. In 1816 he branched out independently.

Having acquired enough money to set himself up as an artist, he graduated to painting panoramic views for the indoor 'in the round' displays that were then very popular in the capital. To achieve perfect accuracy of representation, he drew the outlines of the views using a CAMERA OBSCURA, a light-tight box with a lens at one end to cast an image of the view on to a sheet of paper.

In 1822, by using the same means, he introduced the Diorama. In this device, huge transparent and opaque painted screens were set up on a stage. By varying the lighting on the screens, so that one or the other or both were illuminated, he was able to produce the illusion of day and night passing over a scene such as a mountain view or the interior of a church.

Parisian audiences were stunned by the reality of the Diorama, and Daguerre became famous. In 1823, a second Diorama was opened at Regent's Park, in London.

In 1826, Daguerre began experiments to see whether the view projected on the screen of the camera obscura could be recorded on a plate by some chemical means. He had heard of the experiments of a fellow-countryman, Joseph NIÉPCE (1765-1833), who had already succeeded in recording the outlines of transparent objects on light-sensitive plates, and began a correspondence. Niépce was reluctant to divulge details of his method, but in 1829 they signed an agreement to undertake joint research. Niépce, however, died before any workable process had been developed, and Daguerre acquired his materials and continued the experiments.

In Niépce's original process, a silvered copper plate was coated with white bitumen, a weakly light-sensitive substance which hardens upon long exposure, becoming insoluble in turpentine. The light parts of the object were therefore represented by bitumen, while the dark areas appeared as bare silver revealed by the solvent. Niépce darkened the silver by exposing the plate to iodine vapour, producing silver iodide. In 1826, Niépce managed to take a photograph of the view from his window, but exposure took 8 hours on a sunny day.

In 1831, Daguerre discovered that a silver iodide plate was also sensitive to light, but still failed to produce an image in the camera obscura in a reasonable time. The breakthrough came after four more years of work. Having put an unsuccessful plate away in a cupboard, intending to re-coat it for later experiments, he was amazed to take it out a few days later and find a strong image impressed on it. By a process of elimination of the bottles in the cupboard, he discovered that the 'developing' agent was a few drops of mercury from a broken thermometer. The mercury vapour attached itself to the silver iodide affected by light, producing a picture with brilliant highlights.

Daguerreotyping spread rapidly round the world; even in America, the first photograph was taken in September of the same year. In defiance of his government's decision to publicize his process freely, Daguerre had previously managed to get patent rights in England, where the potential for profitable commercial exploitation was very great. The process, however, never became widespread in that country.

By modern standards, the daguerreotype process was very slow. Outdoor scenes in bright sunlight required an exposure of several minutes using the lenses then available, and sitters having their portraits taken had to rest their head in a special clamp. At that time there were no sufficiently strong sources of artificial light, and portrait studios, which could operate only on sunny days, had large windows and glass roofs, making them very hot and uncomfortable.

Daguerre spent the last decade of his life in retirement at Bry-sur-Marne, apparently content to let other experimenters improve his process.

He died in 1851, the year when the English sculptor Frederick Scott Archer (1813-1857) introduced the far superior collodion photographic process.

Below: a copy of the earliest known Daguerreotype still in existence, a still life taken by Louis Daguerre in 1837.

DAIRY INDUSTRY

Dairy production goes back to 3000 BC when milk and butter were supplied to the city states of Mesopotamia from the flocks of sheep herded on the outlying plains.

The development of the dairy industry in Europe was preceded by the advent of livestock improvement methods based on selection of cattle. One of the reasons for the English Enclosure Acts of the 18th century was that selective breeding could not take place as long as animals grazed in common. Town herds were a common feature of the big cities of England during the first half of the 19th century; in London alone, there were estimated to be about 24,000 cows in 1850. In the surrounding counties farmhouse industries manufactured butter by the traditional method of churning cream, and cheese was made in oak tubs or brass cheese kettles. Part of the wealth generated during the industrial revolution was diverted to agriculture, and the 'flying-herd' system of buying heifers in calf, milking them for four years, and then selling for beef became widespread. The extension of railways played an important part in widening the distribution and increasing the amount of milk supplied in England and the United States. It has been estimated that the milk carried to London by rail doubled between 1866 and 1868.

A cheese factory was opened in Koshkonong, Wisconsin as early as 1831, and butter factories were opened in the United States in the 1860s. Further advances in milk preservation were made with Gail Borden's patent for a condensed milk process in 1856, and the introduction of the refrigerated railroad car in 1867. By 1895 *pasteurization,* a mild heat treatment, was being used to extend the keeping life of fresh milk. Today, the dairy industries of the world are huge enterprises. In the European Economic Community alone the dairy herd numbers over 25 million cows. Advances in technology and farming practice are increasing milk yield each year and widening the range of products available to the consumer.

Milk as a food

Although the dairy industries of the technologically advanced countries use the cow as their milk source, all mammals from goats and reindeer to the whale and the porpoise use milk as a source of protein, fat, carbohydrate, mineral matter and vitamins for feeding their young.

The main protein in cow's milk is casein, which constitutes about $3\frac{1}{4}\%$ by weight of the milk. The average fat content of milk is about $3\frac{3}{4}\%$, though some breeds of cow such as the Jersey or South Devon yield a high proportion of cream, and give a milk with a 5% or more fat content. The CARBOHYDRATES are in the form of the milk sugar lactose, which not only provides energy but aids the absorption of calcium by the body. Milk is a good source of the vitamins A and B2. Vitamin A is essential for the growth of body cells and promotes dim-light vision, while vitamin B2 helps to prevent disorders such as angular stomatitis, which results in the cracking of skin at the corners of the mouth.

One British pint (0.57 litre) per day should supply about one quarter of the protein required and all the calcium needed for building bones and teeth. The energy value of 8 pints (4.55 litres) has been estimated as being sufficient to supply the 3000 kilocalories (often referred to simply as Calories) needed daily by the moderately active man.

Milking

Mechanical milking machines are used in which a cup fits around the udder and withdraws milk by intermittent suction (see MILKING MACHINE). It is vital to cool the raw milk to below 50°F (10°C) at once to prevent the growth of naturally occurring bacteria, which can amount to as many as 500 per millilitre in a healthy cow. The control of infection is very highly developed. In the United Kingdom a tuberculosis-free herd has been maintained by a national programme of testing, and steps to eliminate brucellosis are under way.

Hygienic practice in handling is essential in controlling the quality of milk. For example, the milking cups should be washed with a disinfectant formulated with chlorine or iodine and all milk processing equipment should be washed with a detergent at a temperature of 140°F (60°C) to 170°F (77°C) to remove fat and mineral deposits. The bacteria are eliminated by using either steam or one of the proprietary chemical agents which are known collectively as *biocides.*

Milk is delivered to the dairy in refrigerated bulk tankers. On arrival the milk in each tanker is mixed by using compressed air and a sample taken for testing. Apart from testing for compositional quality, the milk is subjected to the Resazurin test. A mauve dye called Resazurin is added to a milk sample, and the extent to which it turns pink is the measure of the bacteriological quality.

Milk processing

Deterioration of milk is caused by bacteria which convert the lactose to lactic acid, resulting in

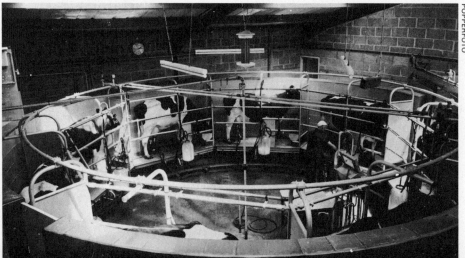

Left: a Carousel Milking Unit at Alexander's Farm, Eynsford. The Carousel turns on a rail, making one revolution in the time it takes to milk one cow. Then the cow gets off and another cow gets on. All the plumbing must be thoroughly cleaned after use with germicidal chemicals and the milk must be cooled to prevent bacterial growth. Methods like these are necessary to provide all the milk products needed. Britain alone uses seven to nine million tons of milk each year.

Right: removing a ton of butter from a churn in Australia.

POPPERFOTO

souring. Pasteurization will destroy these bacteria. Most dairies use the *high temperature short time* (HTST) process for the continuous pasteurization of milk. The milk is heated to 161°F (71°C) and held at that temperature for fifteen seconds. The temperature is measured with a thermocouple, and if the required temperature has not been reached, a flow diversion valve recycles the milk for further heating. Immediate cooling of the milk is essential after pasteurization, and this is accomplished by using the hot milk to partially heat the incoming cold milk, which also saves energy. The bottles are filled automatically with the milk at a temperature of 38°F (3°C).

Pasteurized milk has a life of about three days in a refrigerator, but this can be extended to at least seven days by the sterilization process, which also kills the proteolytic bacteria which can break down the milk proteins and give the milk an offensive taste. To sterilize the milk, it is first of all homogenized. This is a process of forcing the milk through small openings to break up the fat globules, so that the cream is thoroughly mixed in and will no longer separate. (In the USA most milk sold in shops is homogenized.) Then it is steam heated at 220°F (104°C) for at least twenty minutes. In Britain, it is steamed in the familiar long-necked bottles in which it is sold in the shops, and the bottles are immediately tightly capped. Sterilized milk may develop a cooked flavour.

A comparatively recent innovation is the *ultra high temperature* (UHT) process, also known as Uperisation, in which steam is injected into the milk to raise the temperature to 300°F (150°C) at which it is held for about three seconds. The added water content from the steam is removed by expanding the sterilized milk into a flash evaporator (a vacuum) which also cools the milk. UHT milk will keep for several months unrefrigerated, unless it is open to the air.

Cream Cream is rich in milk fat and vitamin A, but most of the calcium stays in the skim milk left after cream separation. To separate the cream, whole milk is warmed to about 120°F (49°C) and passed through a centrifuge, where it passes over a stack of rapidly rotating discs. The discs throw the heavier skim milk to the walls of the centrifuge from which it leaves by a separate outlet pipe. The machine is adjustable for the weight of the cream desired. Single cream and double cream should have a fat content of 18% and 48% respectively; both creams are pasteurized at 175°F (79.5°C) to give a storage life of 4 days in a refrigerator. Cream is also homogenized to thicken it and ensure even distribution of the fat. A grade of cream with 35% fat is ideal for making whipped cream for cake and dessert decoration.

Whey is the liquid residue from cheese making, and it contains a small amount of fat which can be separated to make whey cream. Soured cream is made from single cream by treating it with a strain of bacteria to develop the piquancy.

Butter processing Cream for the manufacture of butter may be used directly ('sweet cream') or ripened by cultures such as *streptococcus paracitrovorus* thus producing the conditions for flavour development and the elimination of undesirable taints.

Cold water is added to the cultured cream to give a temperature between 12°C (54°F) and 17°C (63°F). After the cream has been strained, churning at slow speed commences and when all the air has been excluded, the churning rate is increased to give small grains of butter after about 20 minutes. A small amount of water, a degree or two below the churning temperature, is added to prevent butter lump formation and the churning is continued until the required grain size is reached.

The liquid residue, or buttermilk, is separated by pumping through a sieve and the butter is thoroughly washed until a clear filtrate is obtained. The final stages of processing involve the working of the butter to develop texture and expel excess moisture.

Salt is frequently added in amounts up to 5% by weight to improve flavour and prolong shelf life. The natural colour of the butter is due to the pigment carotene and since the cream of Jersey and Guernsey cows are rich in this pigment they give a deeply coloured butter. Grass and green vegetables are the best sources of carotene but cereal-fed cows tend to give a pale butter because of the lower carotene content in the cereal. The colour, however, may be supplemented by adding the pigment annatto, which is also used frequently in margarine manufacture.

Cheese In the manufacture of a hard cheese, such as Cheddar, pasteurized whole milk is soured by converting some of the lactose into lactic acid with a culture—a carefully prepared growth—of lactic acid bacteria. Rennet, a coagulant, is added to turn the milk proteins into a curd, which is subsequently cut into ½ inch (13 mm) cubes to allow the liquid residue, or whey, to separate.

The curd is shrunk and hardened by slowly raising the temperature to 100°F (38°C) after which the curd particles settle into a matted mass at the bottom of the cheese vat. The whey is drained off and the curd cut into blocks which are piled on top of one another to remove more whey under pressure. The method of treatment during piling or *cheddaring* varies from place to place, but always involves further cutting, turning and piling to a greater height. Often a weight is placed on top to assist drainage.

The blocks are then milled (cut) into small pieces and salted

to preserve and flavour the final cheese. After the curd has been pressed in moulds for up to 48 hours, it is removed to the ripening room in which it is held at a temperature of 50°F to 60°F (10 to 16°C) and controlled humidity. The cheese matures over a period of three to six months as a result of the action of bacteria and enzymes in the cheese.

A high moisture content is obtained in the manufacture of the soft cheese Camembert by omitting the pressure and heating stages. Also, the surface of the cheese is inoculated with the mould *penicillium camemberti* which excretes enzymes into the cheese, resulting in the characteristic flavour. Blue-veined cheese, such as Stilton, utilizes the mould *penicillium roqueforti* but in this case, mould growth is encouraged in the interior of the cheese by piercing with metal wires to provide the air supply required by the mould.

Cottage cheese, made from pasteurized fat-free milk, is an example of the lactic type which relies upon acidity to coagulate the milk protein. A culture of lactic acid bacteria is added to the milk to develop acidity, and rennet is normally not used. The particulate texture of the cheese is achieved by washing the curd with skim milk, which is often fortified with dry skim milk powder. The resulting cheese has a moisture content of between 70% and 80%, a low calorific value and a short keeping time.

Processed cheese is a combination of cheese with additives for consistency and flavour which is melted and poured into retail containers.

Condensed and evaporated milk
Both of these products involve concentration by evaporation at temperatures in the range 130°F (54°C) to 145°F (63°C) under a vacuum. Condensed milk is a sweetened product relying on a sugar concentration of about 43% to preserve the canned product. Evaporated milk is preserved by sterilizing the cans of milk in a steam retort at 240°F (115°C) for about 20 minutes.

The texture of condensed milk is achieved by seeding with a small quantity of lactose crystals and by slow cooling of the concentrated product to 75°F (24°C), followed by further cooling with agitation to about 60°F (16°C). Since canned condensed milk is not heat treated it is vital that hygienic operation should apply at all stages of processing, and it is customary to steam sterilize the cans and lids before filling. Evaporated milk should keep for about two years provided the temperature is kept below 60°F (16°C). At storage temperatures above 70°F (21°C) there is the possibility of browning occurring which, though harmless, does not appeal to the consumer.

Dried milk
Milk fortified with vitamin D and dried on steam-heated rollers is used for infant foods, but the most common technique for drying milk is by *spray drying*.

Before skim milk can be spray dried the milk solids content must be increased to about 40% by vacuum evaporation. After this the concentrated milk is preheated to about 150°F (66°C) and sprayed into an air heated drying chamber by using a nozzle or a spinning wheel. The milk droplets are dried by the air at a temperature of about 380°F (190°C) and pneumatically conveyed from the bottom of the drying chamber to the packaging room. The final product has a moisture content of less than 5%.

One of the problems with the early spray dried milk powders was their poor reconstitution properties when added to beverages such as tea or coffee. This is solved by passing the milk powder through a turbulent air stream before it is completely dry. The milk particles collide with one another and form clusters of milk powder which are then finally dried and packaged. This process is known as *agglomeration* and results in the familiar 'instant' milk powder.

Yoghurt
The unique flavour and texture of yoghurt is obtained by treating milk with a culture of *lactobacillus bulgaricus* and *streptococcus thermophilus*. The milk should be pasteurized at 194°F (90°C) before inoculation to kill the

Below: a bacterial culture called a starter is first added to milk to start the cheese making process. This photograph shows the next step, the addition of rennet to coagulate the milk.

Below: the basic cheese is cut into cubes to adjust the moisture and acidic content. Cutting it into cubes exposes more of the surface area to the air, which is controlled for humidity and temperature.

NATIONAL DAIRY COUNCIL

NATIONAL DAIRY COUNCIL

Top: instantisers, also called fluid bed driers. These devices remove residual moisture from dried milk and crystallize the lactose, thus improving the solubility. Above: milk pasteurizing equipment. Milk handling facilities, especially plumbing, are usually made of stainless steel because it is easy to keep clean.

Below: veining Stilton cheese by poking holes in it with copper pipes. Veining certain cheeses in order to allow access by 'good' bacteria is essential for characteristic texture, colour and flavour.

natural organisms of the milk, some of which could produce taints in the yoghurt.

After the milk has been cooled to 100°F (43°C), it is inoculated with the culture and put into sterile retail cartons, and the culture allowed to develop at that temperature for several hours. The finished product must be cooled to below 41°F (5°C); otherwise the culture will remain active and the yoghurt become increasingly acidic.

The milk is frequently fortified with up to 3% skim milk powder to supplement the protein content and give a means of controlling the viscosity of the yoghurt. A low fat natural yoghurt will contain just over 1% and have about 65 calories per 100 grammes. In the case of fruit yoghurts, the yoghurt is incubated in bulk before it is transferred into cartons, and the fruit added after cooling.

Current production and future trends The United States uses about 35 million tons of milk each year, and of this $7\frac{1}{2}$% is used in ice cream alone. Britain, France and West Germany each use between seven and nine million tons. Smaller countries have smaller outputs, but their dairy industries play a larger role in their national economies.

Research is continuing in the development of new products based on milk. Powdered yoghurt mixtures may become available requiring only the addition of water; in Germany, the shelf life of conventional yoghurt has been greatly extended by a pasteurizing process. Ultra high temperature processes have made possible products such as canned custard.

Cheese whey used to be a troublesome by-product, because it depleted the oxygen supply of rivers into which it was discharged. Now, however, valuable nutrients such as protein, mineral salts and lactose are extracted by filtration, leaving a much cleaner effluent. The USA alone produces 22,000 million pounds (1000 million kg) of whey of which only a third is utilized; there is great scope for the further development of new products and processes.

Below: testing Stilton for humidity in the air-conditioned storage chamber. The cheese is graded for smell, texture and so on. It is stored for three to six months while it matures.

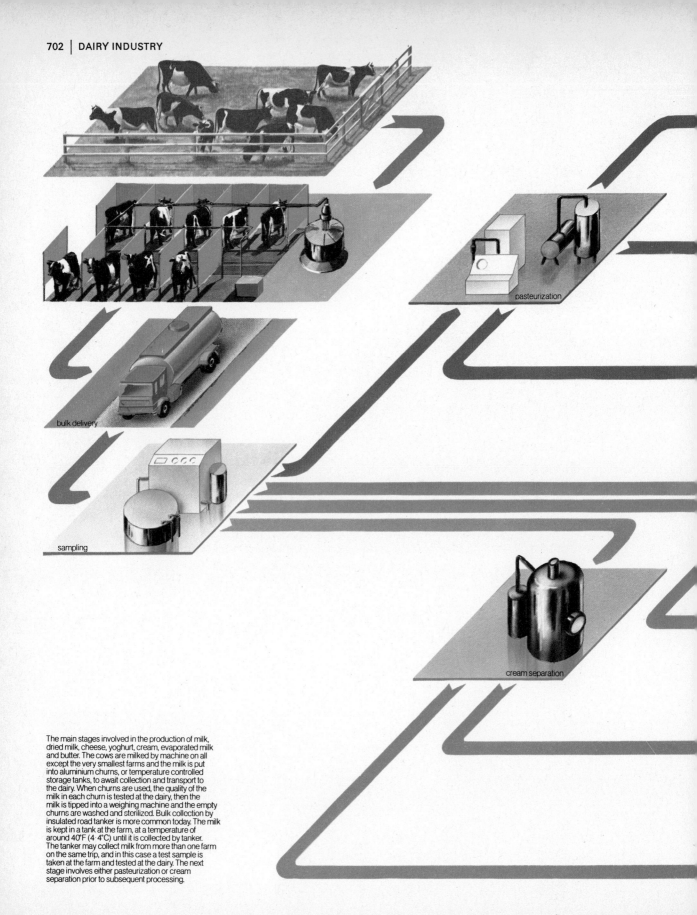

bulk delivery

sampling

pasteurization

cream separation

The main stages involved in the production of milk, dried milk, cheese, yoghurt, cream, evaporated milk and butter. The cows are milked by machine on all except the very smallest farms and the milk is put into aluminium churns, or temperature controlled storage tanks, to await collection and transport to the dairy. When churns are used, the quality of the milk in each churn is tested at the dairy, then the milk is tipped into a weighing machine and the empty churns are washed and sterilized. Bulk collection by insulated road tanker is more common today. The milk is kept in a tank at the farm, at a temperature of around 40°F (4·4°C) until it is collected by tanker. The tanker may collect milk from more than one farm on the same trip, and in this case a test sample is taken at the farm and tested at the dairy. The next stage involves either pasteurization or cream separation prior to subsequent processing.

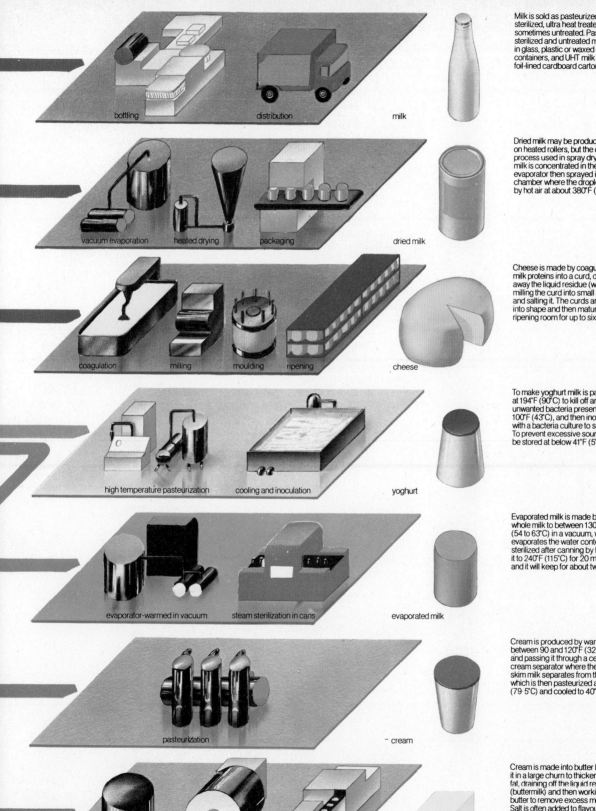

Milk is sold as pasteurized, sterilized, ultra heat treated, or sometimes untreated. Pasteurized, sterilized and untreated milk is sold in glass, plastic or waxed cardboard containers, and UHT milk is sold in foil-lined cardboard cartons.

bottling   distribution   milk

Dried milk may be produced by drying on heated rollers, but the commonest process used in spray drying. The milk is concentrated in the vacuum evaporator then sprayed into a heated chamber where the droplets are dried by hot air at about 380°F (190°C).

vacuum evaporation   heated drying   packaging   dried milk

Cheese is made by coagulating the milk proteins into a curd, draining away the liquid residue (whey), then milling the curd into small pieces and salting it. The curds are moulded into shape and then matured in a ripening room for up to six months.

coagulation   milling   moulding   ripening   cheese

To make yoghurt milk is pasteurized at 194°F (90°C) to kill off any unwanted bacteria present, cooled to 100°F (43°C), and then inoculated with a bacteria culture to sour it. To prevent excessive souring it must be stored at below 41°F (5°C).

high temperature pasteurization   cooling and inoculation   yoghurt

Evaporated milk is made by heating whole milk to between 130 and 145°F (54 to 63°C) in a vacuum, which evaporates the water content. It is sterilized after canning by heating it to 240°F (115°C) for 20 minutes, and it will keep for about two years.

evaporator-warmed in vacuum   steam sterilization in cans   evaporated milk

Cream is produced by warming milk to between 90 and 120°F (32 to 49°C), and passing it through a centrifugal cream separator where the heavier skim milk separates from the cream, which is then pasteurized at 175°F (79·5°C) and cooled to 40°F (4·4°C).

pasteurization   cream

Cream is made into butter by turning it in a large churn to thicken the fat, draining off the liquid residue (buttermilk) and then working the butter to remove excess moisture. Salt is often added to flavour it and prolong its shelf life.

storage   churn   packaging   butter

DALTON, John (1766-1844)

John Dalton was a chemist and meteorologist. He is now famous for the atomic theory, and for his law of partial pressure (see GAS LAWS). These two apparently unrelated ideas stem from the love of METEOROLOGY Dalton acquired as a boy.

John Dalton was born on 6 September, 1766. His father was a Quaker woolweaver in Eaglesfield, near Cockermouth in Cumberland. He went to school until he was 12, when he began teaching, first at a school which he opened himself and then at a school in Kendal. Throughout his life he remained a Quaker.

Dalton acquired an interest in meteorology from a teacher, Elihu Robinson. From 1787 until he died he kept a meteorological diary and he wrote a book on meteorology which was published shortly after leaving Kendal in 1793. In that year he went to Manchester to be a tutor at New College, a position he was to hold for six years. After arriving in Manchester, Dalton published a description of his peculiar eyesight; his complaint is now called Daltonism or colour blindness. The description was the first good account of the affliction and brought it to general attention. To Dalton leaves appeared to have the same colour as red sealing wax, and the sky appeared pink.

In June 1800 John Dalton resigned from New College so that he could concentrate on his researches. He supported himself by giving private lessons at 1s 6d, 2s and, when famous, at 2s 6d an hour. Dalton was a man of regular habits and meticulous about his dress. He usually wore knee breeches, grey stockings, buckled shoes, and a white neck cloth, and he carried a gold tipped cane. Every day, except Sundays and

Top right: a table of Dalton's atomic symbols. It can be seen that they do not quite correspond to those of today, but it was a start.

Right: Dalton drew this diagram to explain why the curved appearance of the aurora was due to the earth's curvature. The phenonemon is caused by particle collisions in the air 65 to 500 miles (105 to 800 km) high, giving off light, often as brilliant yellow-green arcs.

Below: Dalton stirring up the bottom of a pond to liberate marsh gas (mainly methane), for a boy to collect in upturned jars. This gas is produced by decaying vegetation; sometimes it ignites spontaneously.

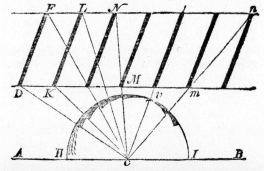

Thursdays, he worked in the laboratory from 8 am until 9 pm. On Thursday afternoons he went for a game of bowls at the 'Dog and Partridge'. After work he had supper and would then light his pipe and discuss the day's affairs with the Johns, the family in whose house he rented a room. Dalton was a silent, rather undemonstrative man and he never married.

His interest in meteorology led him to experiment with water and gases. In 1801 he read a series of papers to the Manchester Literary and Philosophical Society of which he was to become president in 1817. In one of them Dalton announced the law of partial pressures. This states that the pressure of a gas in a mixture is equal to the pressure it would exert if it occupied the same volume alone at the same temperature. The total of these partial pressures gives the pressure of the gas mixture. He also described a HYGROMETER he had designed to measure the humidity and argued that air is a mixture of gases, including water vapour, and not a single compound.

On his birthday in 1803, Dalton made an entry in his notebook in which he derived a list of atomic weights. On the next few pages he wrote out the atomic theory. There has been considerable debate as to how Dalton arrived at this, but it was probably the solubility of gases that led him to the theory. Dalton's notebooks and other documents were destroyed during World War 2, but they had been well examined by then. He did not publish the theory straight away, but mentioned it to another chemist, Thomas Thomson, who described it in a book. The next year Dalton described the atomic theory in his own textbook, *A New System of Chemical Philosophy*, using his own chemical symbols. The main postulates were: matter consists of indivisible atoms; all atoms of a given element are identical in weight and in every other property; different elements have different kinds of atoms of different weight; atoms are indestructible and merely rearrange themselves in chemical reactions (this was the basis of his law of multiple proportion).

The theory made him famous. He was invited to lecture in most of the learned centres, and when he visited Paris he was greeted by numerous eminent French scientists and shown AMPÈRE's apparatus for demonstrating electromagnetic phenomena. In 1822 he was elected a Fellow of the Royal Society and later became their first Royal Medallist. The French Academy of Science, in 1830, elected him one of its eight foreign associates, a great honour.

Dalton's daily routine did not change after he became famous. He published some more work on chemistry and meteorology, and republished his meteorological book. The first serious illness in Dalton's life occured in 1837 when he suffered a paralytic attack. In May 1844 he had an apoplectic attack and on 27 July he was found dead in his bed, having just made an entry in his diary about the weather. Forty thousand people filed past his coffin and there was a 100 carriage funeral procession.

According to his own account Dalton was not brilliant, but won his achievements by perseverance. His school record shows this to be true. He published 140 papers but very few are remembered. The atomic theory, however, was a triumph. By 1800 there existed numerous rules and laws about chemical reactions. In a delightfully simple way the atomic theory explained them all and led to the discovery of more. It is for this reason that Dalton is best remembered. A statue was erected to his memory in Manchester.

DAMP PROOFING METHODS

Dampness caused by external moisture permeating the structure of a building causes deterioration of the fabric, and encourages decay through fungoidal diseases. It causes damage to internal and external decoration, as well as to furniture and fittings.

By far the most common dampness problem in Britain is *rising damp,* or penetration of the building's structure by dampness from the soil. The dampness 'climbs' the mortar and brickwork by capillary action, and is often indicated by an unsightly stain on an internal wall, or by paper peeling from it. Dampness occurring internally often results in concentrations of dissolved *hygroscopic* (water absorbing) salts at the plaster surface. Unless the plaster is renewed these salts absorb moisture from humid air, further dampening the wall.

Where the climate is drier, as in most parts of the USA for example, rising damp is not much of a problem. In Britain, new buildings are usually designed with anti-dampness features; most instances of rising dampness are found in older buildings. Construction features, too, are a factor. In the USA houses are usually built of wood, which is less expensive there and not prone to rising damp; even brick houses consist of a brick outer facing with a wooden framework inside, and plaster is rarely applied directly to a masonry surface.

Damp proofing will not, by itself, dry out a structure or repair damage already done, but prevents further occurrence. There are four methods of damp proofing: installation of a damp proof course (DPC), electro-osmosis, silicone penetration and syphonage.

Damp proof course (DPC)
A DPC is often installed in new buildings as they are constructed. It is a barrier layer of comparatively impervious material, such as felt impregnated with bitumen, a bituminous liquid membrane, or heavy duty (perhaps 500 gauge) polythene sheeting.

The barrier is laid horizontally in all exterior walls, sandwiched between two layers of mortar approximately six inches (150 mm) above ground level, in a continuous ribbon.

Laying a chemical damp proof course by boring holes into a wall and pouring in a silicone-based solution which permeates the brickwork. The water-repellent silicone remains after the water evaporates.

SGB GROUP

1 moisture from the ground
2 moisture from 'under-floor' area
3 corroded masonry
4 high earth banks retain moisture

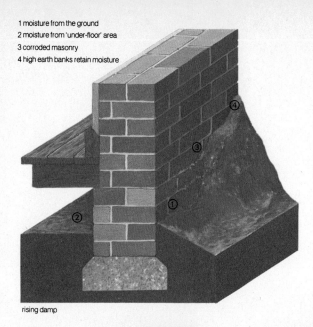

rising damp

The floors on the ground level also incorporate a layer of the impervious material which is lapped into the DPC in the walls.

A DPC can be installed in an older building. This necessitates the removal of bricks, one or two at a time, usually with a chain saw. The barrier is inserted; it may be one of the kinds of impervious sheeting or sometimes hard engineering bricks. An impervious barrier can be installed to combat rising damp in floors laid directly on earth; either a resin with an epoxy-pitch base is used to cover the floor, or the floor is lifted and then relaid on a bituminous membrane or polythene sheeting.

Electro-osmosis This method of damp proofing relies on the fact that where an electrical potential difference exists there is a flow of moisture, so by introducing suitable electrodes into the system it is possible to inhibit moisture movement up a porous wall. There are two types, passive and active, although the passive system is not strictly electro-osmotic. In the passive method, copper strip $\frac{1}{2}$ inch (13 mm) wide is embedded into the wall at the normal DPC level. The strip is connected to electrodes, also of copper, which are driven into the earth, thereby earthing the potential difference of the building and preventing the moisture from rising.

DIAGRAM

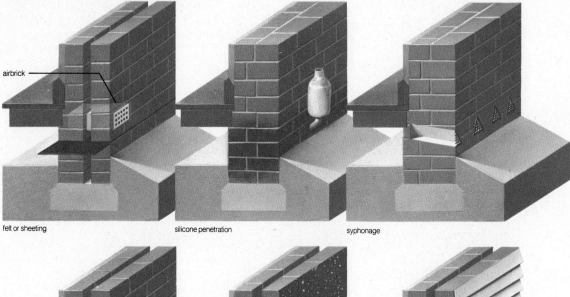

airbrick

felt or sheeting

silicone penetration

syphonage

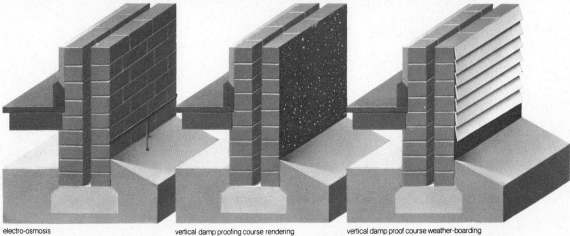

electro-osmosis

vertical damp proofing course rendering

vertical damp proof course weather-boarding

Protection against rising damp can be achieved by inserting a strip of impermeable material between layers of bricks above ground level. A series of small holes can be drilled at the same level and a water repellent silicone solution allowed to permeate the brick from bottles.

Syphonage drains excess water through sloping pipes. A copper strip embedded in the wall and earthed to the ground counteracts osmotic pressure, preventing the water from rising. An outer rendering in a special material or weatherboarding is also very effective.

In active methods an external electrical source is applied between the electrodes to produce the potential (about 2 to 20V DC). The scientific basis on which this method works is not fully understood; some authorities believe, for instance, that a larger power rating (several thousand volts) should, in theory, be necessary.

Silicone penetration This method necessitates the drilling of a series of holes along the wall at DPC level. The holes are spaced at nine inch (230 mm) intervals; a water repellent, silicone-based solution is poured into the holes from small bottles fitted to the holes. The bottles are replenished until the porous brickwork is permeated with the fluid. The solution is often a siliconate-latex solution in order to easily penetrate the brickwork; it subsequently becomes water repellent when the water evaporates.

Syphonage Hollow pipes of porous clay two inches (51 mm) in diameter and less than the wall thickness in length are embedded in mortar in pre-drilled holes; the holes run down out of the wall at a 30° angle. Rising moisture penetrates the pipes, accumulates and drains from the wall. A louvred grille shields the pipe ends from rainwater.

This method may be used in conjunction with silicone penetration, with the pipes fitted below the silicone level to provide drainage of the water prevented from rising.

Rain penetration In solid wall structures, internal dampness may be caused by penetration of the brickwork by rainwater. Wall exteriors can be waterproofed, in effect by applying a vertical DPC. The wall is first renovated as necessary; cracks or fractures are repaired and vulnerable points sealed. Joints around window and door frames are caulked with a mastic compound, and a waterproof sealant is applied to the wall by spraying or painting. These can be either translucent or coloured for decorative effect.

More radical waterproofing is effected by rendering with pebble dash or tyrolean (another type of composite material incorporating fine aggregate) compounds, or by weatherboarding or tiling.

The type of structural dampness requiring treatment should not be confused with ordinary condensation, such as moisture which appears on the wall when filling a bathtub with hot water in a cold room.

Above: an operative is heating a wall to dry it out and assist penetration of the milky latex-siliconate being injected through the nozzles. Clay or silt which has lodged in the base of the wall is impeding penetration, except with the second nozzle from the right.

DATA STORAGE

Digital COMPUTERS have two main data storage areas, the main MEMORY and the backing store, which can be compared to a filing centre for storing papers. With the enormous amounts of data handled by a modern computer it is impractical to store it all in the main memory, mainly because of the high cost and the amount of space needed to install sufficient memory units to meet the user's requirements.

Files of data may be held in the form of punched cards or paper tape, but these storage media are not generally regarded as backing stores. This term is applied only to devices linked directly to the computer processor and using MAGNETIC TAPE, drums or disks, or in some cases plastic cards coated with a magnetic iron oxide film. Tapes and disks are the most common forms of backing store, but many computers use more than one type of store as each has certain inherent advantages and limitations which make it better suited to particular applications.

Recording and playback The data is recorded (the term used is *written*) on to the magnetic coating of the tapes, disks, drums and cards and played back (*read*) from it by means of sets of read-write heads. These operate, in principle, in a similar way to the record and playback heads on a TAPE RECORDER. The heads contain electromagnetic coils which perform the reading and writing function. Signal pulses from the central processor are fed to the recording coils, and the magnetic fields produced in the coils magnetize the areas of the recording medium next to them. The data is thus recorded in the form of a series of magnetic spots (*bits*) on the oxide coating; when these move past the coils of the read head they induce electric currents in the windings and the resultant signals can then be 'read' by the processor. The magnetized spots represent either a '1' or a '0'—the two symbols used in the binary code of LOGIC CIRCUITS. This can be done by arranging for the recording signals to flow in one direction for a '1' and in the opposite direction for a '0'. The direction in which the spots are magnetized depends on the direction of the magnetizing current, so this arrangement will produce two distinct types of magnetic spot, one for each binary digit or *bit*, which in turn will induce two different directions of current flow in the read heads.

In practice the read and write heads are usually physically combined in one read-write head assembly, and in some cases the same set of coils may be used for both reading and writing, being switched electronically from one mode to the other as instructed by the processor. As there are only two types of bit recorded, and each bit is fully magnetized in one direction or the other, there is no need for an erase head as there is on a tape recorder.

Magnetic tape The magnetic tape used on computers resembles that used on sound recorders, but is usually 2400 feet (732 m) long and $\frac{1}{2}$ inch (13 mm) wide, wound on 10 inch (25.4 cm) diameter spools. (Some cut-price unbranded 'white-box' recording tapes are sub-standard computer tapes cut lengthwise to $\frac{1}{4}$ inch (6.4 mm) width and wound on to standard tape recorder spools.) Magnetic tape units use 7 or 9 tracks running along the length of the tape, and some can handle both 7 and 9 track requirements. The head assembly contains a read-write head for each track so that the machine can read or write all tracks simultaneously. All tracks are usable for data recording except one, which is the one in which the *parity* bits are written. To give a built-in accuracy check on each row of bits written across the tape, the controlling system counts the number of '1's in a row before it is written, and writes either a '1' or a '0' in the parity track so that the total number of '1's in each row is always an odd number (*odd bit parity*) or an even number (*even bit parity*). The row of bits is read immediately after writing, and if the parity check is incorrect, which means that the data bits have been wrongly written, the tape is backspaced and the row of bits re-written. If the error is still present when the parity is checked again, the presence of the error can be indicated to the machine operator.

Data is written in short blocks, with a small space left between each one, and the precision of the read-write heads allows very dense packing of the data. The space between the blocks of data allows the unit to operate one block at a time if necessary, as it allows the machine time to stop the tape at the end of one block and restart it again and reach proper operating speed before the next block is read.

With recording densities of as much as 1600 bytes (rows of bits) per inch (about 630 bytes per cm) and tape speeds of 200 inches per second (508 cm per second) the tapes must be stopped and started with great precision. In the latest tape drives this is achieved by the use of motors with very light moving parts, high acceleration and deceleration speeds, and very precise braking mechanisms. To reduce the amount of fast stopping and starting and changes of direction of the tape spools, and to permit more precise handling of the tape, tape reservoirs are provided between each spool and the head area. The tape runs down from each spool into a column placed directly below it, and is drawn back up out of it by the tape drive capstans when needed. Sensing devices in the reservoir columns ensure that the amount of tape in each column is maintained at an optimum level, the spool drive motors feeding more tape in or out of the columns as necessary.

The number of tape drives used depends on the size and requirements of the computer system. Control units link the drives to the central processor, each control unit serving several drives. One of the tape reels is fixed permanently into the drive unit, and the other is removable, so that the recorded files of data can be removed from the machines when not needed, freeing them for further work. The tapes of data prepared on one computer can be processed on any other similar machine, giving a measure of flexibility to this method of data storage. To prevent irretrievable loss of important data, most users have more than one copy of important tapes, so that if one is lost or damaged there is always a spare available.

Magnetic disks Magnetic disks are used in sets or packs which look like a stack of gramophone [phonograph] records with a small space between each one. They are made of metal with a magnetic coating on both surfaces and a pack, typically of 11 disks, is placed on the central spindle of the drive unit, which runs at a speed of about 2400 revs/min. All the surfaces except the top and bottom of the stack are used for data storage and there is a read-write head for each. The heads are carried on arms and lightly spring loaded towards the disk surfaces, but they do not actually touch them. The slipstream created by the rapidly rotating disks is sufficient to keep the head 'floating' about one micron (one millionth of a metre) away from the disk. As there is no physical contact between the

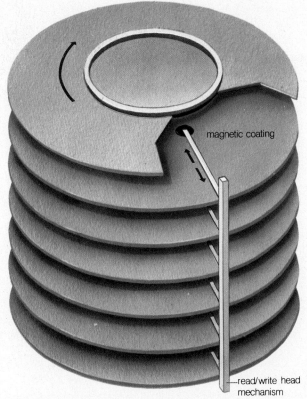

magnetic coating

read/write head mechanism

Top: a row of magnetic tape units. The tapes are loaded onto the left hand hubs, the empty reels normally being left permanently in place.

Above: disk drive units (foreground) and magnetic tape units. The disk packs are kept in the round plastic cases when not in use.

A simplified diagram of a disk pack and read write heads. The method of moving the heads varies according to the design.

disks and the heads there is no friction or wear and the heads can be positioned quickly and precisely.

The data is recorded in concentric tracks on the disk surfaces with a space of about 0.005 inch (0.127 mm) between each one. Data is recorded in short blocks and is accessed (made available) by moving the read-write heads to the appropriate position. Modern disk systems can access a given item of data in as little as 30 milliseconds, with a read-write time of 800,000 bytes per second and a pack capacity of 200 million bytes.

As with tape units, a 'string' of drives is supervised by a control unit, and as the heads can be retracted fully from the disk packs on most drives the packs are removable and interchangeable.

Magnetic drums Magnetic drums, which are metal cylinders with an external magnetic coating, were introduced before disks but have now been effectively superseded by them. The drum rotates on a horizontal or vertical spindle at a speed of up to 7000 revs/min. Tracks run round the circumference and a number of read-write heads, each serving a group of adjacent tracks, are spaced along the length of the cylinder. Access time varies from about 4.3 to 35 milliseconds, with corresponding read-write times from 1.5 million to 236,000 bytes per second. Total drum capacity ranges from 1.5 million to 198 million bytes. Drum storage is becoming obsolete because the capital cost is very high for a given capacity. Drums cannot be removed from the drive and so are not interchangeable, and any accidental damage to the drum surface results in expensive replacement compared with the

lower cost of replacing a damaged disk pack.

Magnetic cards Magnetic cards are also contained in packs, individual packs being fed into and removed from the read-write system as required by the program. This type of storage (Card Random Access System) is at present used only by one manufacturer, and there is no reason to suppose that other makers will adopt it.

Access times The greatest practical limitation of magnetic tape systems from the user's point of view is that information is recorded serially on the tapes, that is, in blocks along their length, This is a positive advantage in any application which requires, for instance, successive reference to many names in a file kept in alphabetical order. It is, however, a serious drawback in any application (including all those involving on-line or real time working) where requests for detail are submitted in random order. To extract a given piece of data from a tape system involves winding the tape through until the data is located, which can take a relatively long time. With a disk or drum system all that is needed is to position the heads above the appropriate track, which gives a much faster access time than is possible with a tape unit. Disk and drum systems are designed to give the fast access time needed by on-line and real time applications, and the differing characteristics of the data storage media available is the reason why computer installations may include more than one type.

The total amount of information that may be held in a backing store depends on the number of tapes and disk packs used, and the amount that is available to the computer at any one time depends on how many drive units are installed.

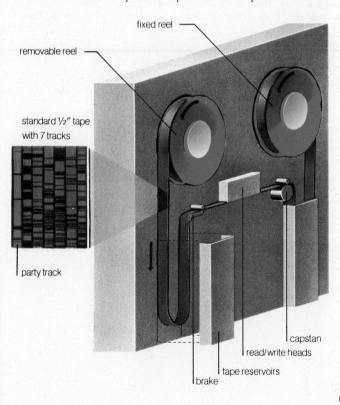

standard ½" tape
with 7 tracks

removable reel

fixed reel

party track

brake

tape reservoirs

read/write heads

capstan

magnetic coating

track

read/write head
mechanism

DIAGRAM

A tape drive unit, showing the brake and capstan used for forward motion of the tape. Those used for reverse motion are not shown.

Simplified arrangement of the magnetic tracks of data bits on a drum unit, and the read-write head asemblies.

DAVY, Sir Humphry (1778-1829)

Sir Humphry Davy was a brilliant and impetuous scientist who made discovery after discovery while still a very young man, and died exhausted at fifty. He invented the miner's safety lamp, which is still in use today, and discovered the chemical elements sodium, potassium and boron.

Davy was born in Penzance, Cornwall, the elder son of a comfortably-off local family, and was given a good education in the hope that he would become a doctor. Even at an early age, he showed a keen intelligence and a great love of nature, and was liked and encouraged by everybody.

After an early interest in poetry, the young Davy turned his attention to science. His actual knowledge of the subject was rather sketchy, but this was less of a disadvantage at the end of the eighteenth century than it would be today, and it also allowed him to make up his own mind about theories that a more thoroughly educated man would have believed unquestioningly.

In 1797 he made friends with an older scientist, Davies Gilbert, who got him a job in the Medical Pneumatic Institution in Clifton, Bristol, a strange establishment which existed to make experiments on the effect of various gases on health. He had already performed his own experiments with nitrous oxide (laughing gas), later to be the first ANAESTHETIC, and he encouraged his friends to try it too. Those who agreed included the poets Coleridge and Southey.

First success Davy experimented with ammonia and nearly killed himself inhaling water gas, a highly poisonous blend of carbon monoxide and hydrogen made by passing steam over red hot charcoal. In 1800 he published his first major work, *Researches, Chemical and Philosophical,* which described his experiments. It was an instant success, and he became well known in scientific circles.

While still only twenty-two, Davy was invited to lecture in London at the Royal Institution. He was a naturally good lecturer and his talks on various topics were attended by the rich and famous; in 1802 he was made a professor. At this time, he was studying such widely different subjects as electric batteries and new methods of tanning leather.

In 1803 he was made a Fellow of the Royal Society; in 1805 he received the Copley medal, and in 1807 he became secretary of the Royal Society. Meanwhile, his research into ELECTROLYSIS led him to discover sodium and potassium (both in 1807), and as a result of his experiments with potassium, another element, boron. In 1808 he invented the electric arc, still used today for welding. He found out the composition of hydrochloric acid and various important facts about the element CHLORINE; at the same time he was carrying on research into agriculture that led to the publication in 1813 of his book *Elements of Agricultural Chemistry,* the standard work on the subject for many years. A book he published a year earlier, *Elements of Chemical Philosophy,* was to have been the first of a series covering the whole of chemistry, but this was too much even for Davy, and he never got any further with the project.

During most of this time, England was at war with France, but such was Davy's fame that this did not stop the Institut de France from awarding him their Bonaparte prize in 1806. Other honours included a knighthood, which he was awarded in 1812.

Shortly after this, he married and set off on a European tour with his wife, in spite of the Napoleonic war. He took with him the young scientist Michael FARADAY, originally hired as a laboratory assistant but soon to be a famous scientist in his

Above: Sir Humphry Davy made many important discoveries in physics, chemistry and medicine. His father was an artisan and sent Davy to grammar school where he developed an interest in the classics and poetry. Following his father's death, however, he was forced to earn his living and became a surgeon's apprentice. A few years later he experimented with gases and their applications in medicine. After this he turned his attention to electrochemistry and during his investigations into electrolysis discovered the elements sodium and potassium and helped to identify chlorine and iodine.

Below: Davy's radiation apparatus for measuring the radiation from a carbon arc lamp, which was another of his inventions.

Top right: Davy carried out the first systematic investigations into explosions in mines and subsequently invented the miner's safety lamp.

Bottom right: Davy's apparatus for gas analysis. His earlier works were concerned with the effects of gases such as nitrous oxide.

own right. During the course of his journey, he used portable scientific equipment to study chlorine compounds and to lay the groundwork for the discovery of the element iodine.

When Davy returned to England in 1815, the Society for Preventing Accidents in Coal Mines commissioned him to study mine explosions and how to prevent them. The result of these researches was that he invented the Davy miner's safety lamp, an oil lamp whose flame was encased in metal gauze, which allowed light and air through but prevented the heat of the flame from starting an explosion by conducting it away. The flame changes colour in the presence of explosive gas; this lamp is still used as a backup to more advanced equipment in detecting gas today.

For this vital invention, Davy was awarded the Royal Society's Gold Medal. The mine owners sent him a lavish set of silver plate, which he later sold to found a trust for awarding the Davy Medal for scientific discoveries. In 1818 he was made a baronet, and in 1820 president of the Royal Society.

His later work included help with the foundation of the Zoological Society and Regent's Park Zoo, and research into the corrosion problems of the copper bottoms of wooden ships. But he was already a prematurely old man and his health was decaying fast. In 1827, he set out for a final tour of Europe, resigning his presidency of the Royal Society to his early friend Davies Gilbert. Apart from a short visit to England in 1828-29 he spent the rest of his time in Europe, dying in Geneva in 1829.

Davy was as far from an academic, narrow-minded scientist as it was possible to be. He maintained a lifelong interest in poetry and literature, fishing and geology. He was a fair artist and illustrated one of his own books, *Salmonia,* a work on salmon fishing, published in 1828. In science, he would turn his mind to almost anything.

DECOMPRESSION techniques

When an aqualung diver is under water, the pressure of the surrounding water on his body increases proportionately with depth (see AQUALUNG). As he ascends, the pressure reduces and his body decompresses; but with decompression comes the danger of decompression sickness—popularly known as the 'bends'. Certain decompression techniques can be carried out to minimize the danger of decompression sickness, but in order to appreciate the necessity for these techniques it is important to know something about the cause and effects of decompression sickness. The cause is a condition called nitrogen absorption, which can best be explained by a simple analogy with carbonated (fizzy) liquid.

Most liquids will absorb and hold a certain amount of gas, either by natural means or artificially. For example, when fizzy drinks such as lemonade are being made, carbon dioxide is added to the liquid in order to make it effervesce. The amount added is more than the liquid would naturally hold at atmospheric pressure, but then the liquid is bottled and sealed, some gas escapes into the small waterless space in the bottle, increasing the pressure and holding the gas in the liquid. When the seal is removed from the bottle the pressure reverts to atmospheric pressure (14.7 psi or 1.01 bar), the liquid suffers a decompression, releasing the excess carbon dioxide it has been holding, and the lemonade fizzes.

While a diver is under water the same process occurs, but in this case the gas is air and the liquid is blood. As the diver descends, he breathes a larger quantity of air in compressed form, and the diver's blood soon becomes saturated with this

Above: Royal Navy personnel pictured with decompression equipment. It should properly be called a 'recompression' chamber, because the diver must be recompressed after he has decompressed too rapidly. The operation of the chamber must be carefully monitored, and information about the depth of the dive is essential.

extra air. While the diver is at depth, the pressure holds this excess air in solution. As the diver rises, the pressure becomes reduced, the excess air comes out of solution, and this is where trouble can start.

Air is comprised mainly of oxygen and nitrogen. Oxygen presents few problems because it is consumed by the body tissues, but nitrogen is a chemically inactive gas that is merely breathed in and out, and never consumed by body tissues. Normally any excess of nitrogen is given off through the lungs while the diver is ascending, but if the ascent is too fast for the blood and lungs to cope, then the nitrogen will react in the same way as the gas in a lemonade bottle when the seal is removed suddenly—the nitrogen will literally 'fizz', causing bubbles to form in the blood. The result is decompression sickness, which in mild cases might be no worse than skin rashes or itches after the dive, or more seriously, excruciating pain, giddiness, loss of balance, unconsciousness, or death.

Decompression techniques Unless the dive is of short duration, in shallow water, it is never possible to eliminate the possibility of decompression sickness. But the correct decompression techniques can reduce the danger to negligible proportions.

Decompression procedure is normally carried out after prior reference to a set of Decompression Tables. These tables calculate the stoppages required at different depths to allow the nitrogen to come out of solution safely—after taking into account the deepest depth and the length of time the diver has been underwater. The tables assume that the rate of ascent never exceeds 18 metres per minute (60 ft/min). If the diver never exceeds a depth of 3 metres (10 ft) there is no necessity for decompression stops, no matter how long he stays underwater. If a diver, however, reaches a depth of 18 metres (60 ft), and spends some 80 minutes underwater before he starts to ascend, then he will have to carry out a 5 minute decompression stop at 6 metres (20 ft) and another for the same period at 3 metres (10 ft). Usually the dive is planned so that the diver has sufficient air in reserve to carry out the correct stops. But if the dive should require a lengthy set of decompression stops, a spare aqualung unit might be hung on a shot line at a depth equal to the first scheduled stop.

For very deep professional or research work, the decompression time might be far too long for a diver to hang on to a line without suffering from exposure. For example, a 210 minute dive to 21 metres (70 ft) will require decompression of 25 minutes at 9 metres (30 ft), 40 minutes at 6 metres (20 ft) and 50 minutes at 3 metres (10 ft). In such cases a decompression chamber might be used. The chamber is built on the same principle as a DIVING BELL, and is dropped on a line to the deepest depth at which the diver is operating. When the diver has finished work, he climbs into the chamber, changes into warm clothes, and the chamber is raised gradually, decompressing the diver safely and in comfort.

As an alternative to tables, the diver can use a decompression meter. This instrument is strapped to the wrist and indicates the stoppages—if any—required by calculating the diver's depth and time underwater.

When the diver surfaces too rapidly and then suffers decompression sickness he must be rushed to a recompression chamber. Once the diver is inside, compressed air is let into the chamber until the diver has been recompressed to a pressure equal to the depth at which he has been diving. Then the pressure is released slowly and the diver is decompressed.

DEEP FREEZE (see refrigerator)

DE-ICING SYSTEMS

A de-icer is a device or material for removing unwanted ice. In many applications, such as the air inlets and other vital parts of aircraft, no ice can be allowed to form at all, and the term is anti-icer rather than de-icer. There are three methods of removing or preventing ice: thermal, chemical and mechanical.

Roads and paths The most familiar method of melting ice on streets is by spreading salt on them. A salt solution has a lower freezing point than pure water, so the salt lowers the freezing point of the ice and it melts. So much salt is used during the winter in some cities that it promotes rusting of vehicle underbodies and becomes an environmental problem when the salt solution enters rivers, lakes and other waters.

Paths are sometimes heated by steam or hot water pipes drawing power from nearby urban or industrial plants; certain stretches of road surfaces in cold climates are heated by electric resistance elements embedded close to the surface. Overpasses, for example, become dangerously slippery sooner than other road surfaces because they are not kept warm by unfrozen ground beneath.

Electrical transmission lines Overhead electric wires are designed to withstand gale-force winds with a coating of ice, but in severe weather each conductor is sometimes overloaded for a short period until the heating effect of the current has raised its temperature above freezing point. Underground cables are usually buried below the frost line.

Vehicles Vehicles often use hot air from the engine. This is the most common method of de-misting or de-icing car windscreens; on some cars the rear window is fitted with electric resistance elements. Alcohol-based chemicals, such as ethylene glycol, are available in bottles or sprays for frozen windscreens. They lower the freezing point of ice, melting it.

On small ships, which can turn over if the superstructure acquires too much ice, the freezing is due to rain or sleet which, because it is pure water, freezes at 0°C (32°F), while the seawater, being salty, freezes at a lower temperature. De-icing ships is difficult, but engine heat, electric heaters and chemicals have all been used.

For electric trains, overhead electric cables need no de-

Top right: laying heating cables in the asphalt surfacing over the concrete deck of the Tinsley Viaduct on the M1, near Sheffield. The cables are mineral insulated, copper sheathed, and supplied with current at 240 volts. They are covered with a hand-laid layer of mastic asphalt, which serves as waterproofing, and then further covered with machine laid asphalt as a wearing course.

Below: if the superstructure of a ship suffers too much ice accretion, the ship can become top heavy. The front of the bridge on this trawler is fitted with rubber-covered heating elements.

icing, as the high voltages used are more than enough to overcome an ice layer. Conducting rails are protected by de-icing trains, which brush or scrape the ice off and apply antifreeze, and by devices such as a de-icing chemical bath which is built into the rail. When freezing temperatures are predicted, a roller can be raised in the bath so that the current-collecting 'shoe' on the locomotive spreads the chemical along the rail. Some rail systems use a plasma torch—a stream of hot ionized gas which flows along a spark discharge between the locomotive and the rail. Switching equipment is protected from freezing by point heaters consisting of a tank of heated oil which is pumped through tubes around it.

Aircraft Aircraft windscreens are protected by a 'sandwich' construction of the glass. The middle layer is a transparent conducting or chemical material, such as a gold film which heats when current is passed through it, or a hollow layer through which hot air can be circulated. Sensing devices keep the glass from overheating and shattering. Control surfaces, air speed pitot tubes, air intakes, propeller blades and so on must be protected to prevent loss of balance or control if the aircraft is likely to fly in icing conditions. It is important that no ice accumulate at all on propeller and turbofan blades, because it can cause dangerous unbalance and can puncture the fuselage when it is thrown off. The blades have electric heaters, or anti-freeze liquid thrown along them by centrifugal force.

A small number of aircraft still use TKS (Tecalemit-Kilfrost-Sheepbridge Stokes) de-icer paste, which was applied to thousands of Allied aircraft during World War 2, but it is difficult to apply in a uniform layer and is eroded by rain and hail. Nowadays low performance aircraft commonly use a mechanical de-icing system originally patented by B F Goodrich, which consists of a strip of rubber applied to the control surface and incorporates ducts inflatable by an engine driven compressor. Inflation of the ducts breaks the ice which is then carried away by the airstream. Faster aircraft use electrical methods or hot air, which is especially abundant from jet engines and can be 'bled' from the engine compartment. The electrical methods use conductors embedded in heat-resistant strips of rubber or other insulating material.

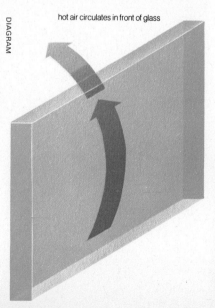

Top: in addition to other de-icing methods, London Transport has a fleet of Electric Sleet locomotives, each fitted with special bogies with de-icing scrapers and crushers, operated from the cab.

Above: a spray-mat heater being tested for electrical overloads. Such mats are used to protect engine intake fairings.

hot air circulates in front of glass

sandwich of gold film conducts current

stick-on element

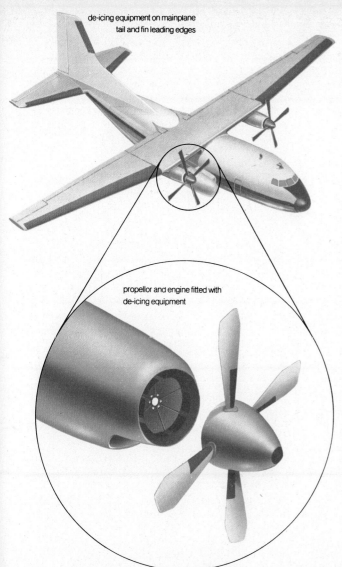

de-icing equipment on mainplane tail and fin leading edges

propellor and engine fitted with de-icing equipment

DELIVERY SYSTEMS

Automatic mechanical methods of moving documents, cash, small parcels and so forth have largely replaced messengers in modern warehouses, office buildings, airline terminals and similar places. With a modern system, documents and parcels can be moved as soon as they are ready instead of having to wait for a messenger to collect them.

A delivery system can be quite simple, such as a gravity chute with a slot on each floor of a building for delivering mail to a basement post room, or an electric lift serving stations one above the other on two or more floors. More complex systems use pneumatic tubes, rails or moving belts.

Pneumatic systems Pneumatic tubes are one of the most common types of delivery system. The system consists of an air pump and a grid of metal or plastic tubes serving a number of stations. The air flow in the system is kept up continuously during working hours, and the delivery-insertion tube at each station has a flap with a seal on it to keep the pressure intact. The air flow will typically be from 800 to 1000 cu ft/min (22.6 to 28.3 m³/min) and the tube diameter can be from 2 to 10 inches (5 to 25 cm). The containers are usually cylindrical, sometimes transparent, and between six inches and three feet (15 and 90 cm) long, with felt rings at each end to ensure a snug fit in the tube.

In a system with more than one delivery point, there are a number of ways of routing the containers. One system is computer operated: the sender pushes buttons sending the destination code to the computer, which keeps track of the container, operating diverting devices in the tube, until it arrives at its proper destination. Another system has rotatable rings on the container itself, each ring bearing metal contacts which strike other contacts inside the tube during transit. These close electrical circuits which operate the diverting devices at tube junction points. Still another system, no

spray-on anti-freeze

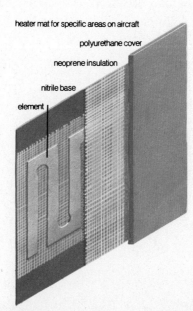

heater mat for specific areas on aircraft

polyurethane cover

neoprene insulation

nitrile base

element

Left: de-icing systems. The simplest type of de-icer is a stream of hot air circulating over the front of the glass. Alternatively the window itself may consist of two layers between which is a very thin sheet of high grade metal, such as gold, through which a current is passed, heating the whole window uniformly. Heating elements can be stuck or bonded onto the window or a chemical antifreeze applied to the whole surface.

Above: de-icing units are installed in critical parts of an aircraft, such as engine intakes. Breaker strips are placed along the leading edges, tail and propeller and are heated intermittently to disperse ice already formed on the surface.

DIALLED DESPATCHES

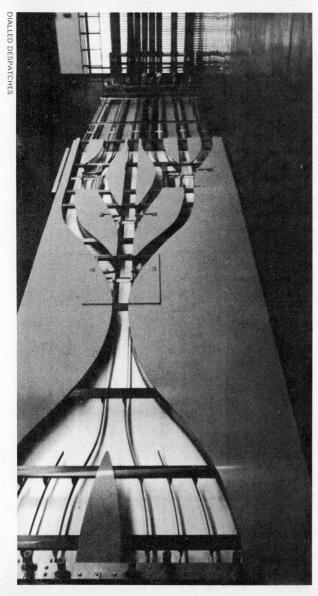

DIALLED DESPATCHES

longer manufactured but still widely in use, has a sound knob on the container with a reed in it. The pitch of the sound can be adjusted by the sender, and the sound is picked up by microphones at the receiving points. When the container reaches its destination, the pitch of the sound triggers the receiving mechanism.

Smaller systems with only one tube can serve twenty stations or so; large systems have up to 2000 stations, with a manual or automatic central exchange. Container speeds can be from 20 to 80 feet/s (6 to 24 m/s); some single tube runs are as long as 8000 feet (2438 m). Systems with over twenty miles (32 km) of tube length are in operation, in which there may be as many as 200 journeys in progress at once.

Special purpose containers can be provided, for example to carry hot samples from a steel furnace to an analytical laboratory. Some systems use rectangular ducts and accept carriers the size of small attaché cases.

Belt systems A system for the transfer of papers, light wallets or folders employs a continuous moving belt running at the bottom of a V-shaped trough made of aluminium or plastic. Diversions are made as required by means of a plough set across the trough.

A heavier, more complex version uses 'addressable' wallets or boxes, with adjustable contacts on the sides of the containers. The contacts are read electrically as the container travels past gates at each station. Payloads of up to 11 lb (5 kg) can be moved by this system. A still larger belt conveyer, up to ten inches (25.4 cm) wide, often combined with a gravity roller system, is used for moving parcels and trays when the system is confined to one or two floors.

Rail systems A wall mounted rail system can be used to send wallets of papers up to 13.5 lb (6 kg) in weight. The rails are narrow tubes of rigid plastic mounted on brackets. The containers are self-propelled flat boxes, each powered by a lightweight rechargeable battery. They are driven by a roller in contact with the rail. A destination code is set by the sender, and junctions in the system are provided by flip-over panels operated by the magnetic destination code. The speed of travel may be 120 feet (36 m) per minute.

Lifts Lifts or elevators for documents or cash or small parcels are installed between vertical stations. The smaller ones may be operated by two cables placed side by side and alternately wound up and down by a small reversible electric motor, by means of push buttons or automatically when the door is closed. Each cable carries a cage for the payload: when one is coming up, the other is coming down. A still larger lift system, carrying loads of up to 30 lb (13.5 kg) as high as 350 feet (106 m), is a continuous chain conveyer, turning on sprockets at the top and bottom of the shaft. The chain is fitted with carrying cars at intervals. The operator sets a dial for the delivery floor and places the load on a dispatching platform. The first empty car to come along automatically picks up the bin and unloads it at the destination, the unloading cycle being initiated by the destination code, which has been transferred to tabs on the side of the car.

Left above: British Steel's Anchor Project at Scunthorpe has 21 miles of pneumatic tube delivery system. It can carry up to 200 messages at a time, including hot steel samples from the plant to the test labs, which are carried in insulated containers.

Left: a junction in Heathrow Airport's Paperlink computer-operated system, complementing the computerized cargo handling scheme.

DEMOLITION TECHNIQUES

The art of demolition is almost as old as the art of building, and the safe demolition of buildings and other structures requires a great deal of skill and expertise. In general, the main ways of demolishing a structure are: dismantling it piece by piece, pulling it down or pushing it over, causing it to collapse under its own weight (often with the assistance of EXPLOSIVES), knocking it down with sledgehammers or a demolition ball, or various combinations of these methods.

Preparation   There are many factors to be considered before the method of demolishing a particular structure can be decided upon. These include its size and its type of construction, the proximity of any adjacent buildings, the time and costs involved, and any particular hazards present such as dangerous weakening of the structure by fire or flood damage.

Once the method has been decided, the first step is to arrange for the disconnection of electricity and telephone cables, gas and water supplies, and drainage and sewer connections. Road and rail bridges often carry cables and pipelines, and these must be disconnected and re-routed by the authorities concerned.

Saleable scrap such as electric cables and copper or lead pipes may be stripped from the building before the main demolition work begins, and many other re-usable items can often be reclaimed from a demolition site as work progresses.

Temporary supports, for example struts and braces, may be needed to prevent an uncontrolled collapse of the structure during demolition, and these, together with protective screens to prevent damage or injury by falling debris, are erected before the main work begins.

Above: hand demolition of a factory chimney. The brickwork is removed progressively, course by course, and the working platform and the scaffolding are lowered as the demolition progresses. The rubble is often dropped down inside the chimney to eliminate danger from flying debris, but it must be regularly cleared from the bottom of the chimney to prevent it building up at ground level and exerting a dangerous pressure on the base of the structure.

Below: dismantling the Temple Bar gate, London, in 1878. It was taken down carefully and later re-erected on a country estate.

To help dispose of the debris from the upper levels of a building, disposal chutes may be provided, and where possible flooring may be taken up to leave a hole through which the debris can be dropped down to ground level.

Hand demolition Demolition of buildings by the use of hand tools, including sledgehammers and pneumatic drills, is ideally carried out in the reverse order to that in which the building was built. Scaffolding platforms are erected, where practicable, to provide a safe area for the operatives to work from. Small structures, such as houses, may be demolished entirely by hand methods, but for taller structures, including chimneys and cooling towers, hand demolition may only be used for the upper sections. This is continued until the height of the structure has been reduced sufficiently to allow the remaining part to be safely demolished by mechanical means (ball, pusher or wire rope).

The roofing is removed first, and heavy beams and girders are cut into sections that are lowered to the ground by a crane or hoist. Large slabs of reinforced concrete are cut into strips, with the cuts running parallel to the main reinforcement. Checks must be carried out before demolishing load-bearing walls or beams to ensure that their removal will not cause an uncontrolled collapse of the remaining structure. Uncontrolled collapse can also be caused by the pressure exerted on the walls by a buildup of fallen debris, so this must be regularly cleared away before a dangerous condition arises.

Mechanical demolition A widely used method of mechanical demolition is by means of a demolition ball, a heavy, pear-shaped cast steel weight suspended from a CRANE or dragline excavator (see EARTHMOVING MACHINERY). The ball is swung against, or dropped on to, the structure to be demolished, but as it cannot be safely used on structures over about 100 ft (30 m) in height, the upper sections are first removed by hand demolition. As most cranes are not built to withstand severe shock loads their use in this type of work is limited to dropping the ball onto horizontal areas such as concrete slabs.

A pusher arm, as the name suggests, can be used to push over brick or masonry structures. The arm is fitted to a large hydraulic EXCAVATOR in place of the bucket, and is typically about 15 ft (5 m) long. As the pusher arm must be applied not more than two feet (60 cm) below the top edge of the wall being demolished, hand demolition may be needed to lower the top of the wall to within reach of the pusher. The latest pushers have a reach of about 45 ft (14 m).

A structure or a part of it may often be demolished by attaching a wire rope or ropes to it, and pulling with a heavy or tracked vehicle or a securely fixed winch. A variety of structures may be demolished in this way, including brick and masonry walls and steel pylons and masts.

Deliberate collapse In certain circumstances, where the site is level and well away from adjacent buildings and the structure is of suitable construction, demolition may be accomplished by the removal of key parts of the structure, causing it to collapse under its own weight. As with all demolition procedures, this is potentially very dangerous and must be carried out under expert supervision.

In the demolition of steel structures, a controlled collapse can be induced by weakening the supporting members and then using a pulling rope to start the collapse. One way of weakening the supports is the thermal reaction process. A

ZEFA

Above: demolition of houses in Germany by use of a demolition ball. The three main ways of using a demolition ball are: dropping it vertically onto horizontal surfaces such as flooring; swinging it against a structure by swivelling the lifting appliance; and swinging it in line with the jib of the appliance by pulling back and then releasing the control line.

Right: a demolition ball in use. With any method of demolition, the public and any adjacent property must be protected from flying debris, in this case by protective screens supported on scaffolding.

JOHN LAING CONSTRUCTION LTD

mixture of a metal oxide and a reducing agent is packed around the girders or columns, and then ignited electrically. Large quantities of heat are generated by the reaction, which soften the steel to a plastic state so that only a small pulling force is needed to cause a collapse.

Another means of creating intense heat for cutting steel (and concrete) is by the use of a THERMIC LANCE. This is a long steel tube filled with steel rods; the end of the tube is preheated, and oxygen is passed through it, reacting with the steel at the heated end and creating an intensely hot flame. One drawback is that the lance burns away rapidly, so protective clothing and goggles must be worn by the operator to protect him as he moves towards the cutting area. Thermic lances, which are very effective cutting tools, are now becoming widely used in many areas of demolition work.

Explosives and bursters

One of the most effective means of causing the collapse of a structure is by the use of explosives. The charges are placed in carefully chosen positions at the base of the structure, so that when they are detonated the supporting members or walls are blasted away and it collapses inwards. Power station cooling towers are well suited to explosive demolition, as they are widest at the base, and the whole tower can be made to fall within the perimeter of the base. The charges are usually detonated electrically, but as there is a risk of the DETONATORS being triggered off by stray electrical signals (from nearby radio transmitters or by electrical storms), it is often necessary to use plain detonators with safety fuzes. Explosives are also used to help remove old concrete or other heavy foundations, and for felling old factory chimneys.

In cases where large blocks of concrete or masonry have to be broken up, but it is not possible to use explosives, an alternative method is the use of *bursters*. These are either gas expansion or hydraulic types. The gas expansion burster consists of a perforated steel cylinder filled with a chemical mixture that vaporizes and expands when ignited electrically. The burster is inserted into a hole drilled in the concrete, which is fractured by the considerable force exerted by the expanding gases when the burster is fired.

The hydraulic burster also fractures the concrete by expansion, but in this case the force is exerted by pistons placed radially around a steel cylinder and forced outwards by hydraulic pressure.

Post-tensioned concrete

Many modern buildings are supported on horizontal concrete beams that are internally tensioned by steel tendons running in ducts. The ducts curve downwards so that the centre of the tendons is lower than the anchorages at each end, forming an inverted bow shape. By applying tension to the tendons an upward force is created because of this curvature, and tension is progressively increased during construction of the building so that the downward load of the structure is balanced by the upward force in the tendons. This creates serious problems when the building has to be demolished: if the load on the beam is reduced the tension in the tendons can force the beam upwards and shatter it, causing an uncontrolled collapse of the building. If tension is removed from the beam it will no longer support the building and a collapse will again occur.

In order to prevent these dangerous situations arising, the tensions in the supporting beams must be gradually reduced to correspond with the reduction in loading caused by the demolition of the superstructure of the building, so that a state of equilibrium is always maintained. As there are several tendons in each beam, reduction of the tension in a beam can be achieved by successive cutting of the tendons.

Before demolition can commence on a building of this type, it is essential that the position and function of all the post-tensioned beams (so called because the tension is applied after the beam has been positioned) is known. It is vital that proper records are kept during construction so that they can be referred to when the building is demolished.

Demolition of all types is inherently dangerous, and must only be carried out by experienced workers under expert supervision.

Left: an old church spire at Beckenham, England, being demolished with explosives. Masonry spires such as this can be demolished by hand, by demolition ball, by deliberate collapse, or by explosives. The method used depends on the height of the spire, whether or not the whole of the church is to be demolished, and the proximity of other buildings, structures or public places. Masonry spires are hollow, with a solid stonework peak.

Right: Shoring left to support an adjacent roadway after the demolition of a large building.

MICHAEL ST MAUR SHEIL

F E BEAUMONT

DENSITOMETER

It is often necessary to measure the brightness and darkness of various regions on a photograph. This is done using a densitometer, and rather than use the final print, the original negative is used. The measurement may be for photographic purposes, as in COLOUR PRINT MAKING; to find out the characteristics of the film itself; or for scientific purposes, such as the measurement of the brightness of stars on a photograph or the variation in thickness in a cell wall in biology. Measurements can also be made on other semi-transparent materials, such as optical FILTERS.

The densitometer consists of a light bulb and a light meter. The sample to be measured is placed between them so that the light meter is measuring its *optical density* (the reverse of transparency, or light transmitted). Density is measured on a *logarithmic* scale: if a sample transmits 10% of the light shining on it, it has a density of 1; if it transmits 1%, it has a density of 2, and so on.

In practice, an optical system concentrates the light from the bulb into a spot, usually about 1/10 inch (2.5 mm) across, but variable in size depending on the instrument and its use. The light meter used is a PHOTOMULTIPLIER TUBE, with an amplifier which operates an ammeter the reading of which depends on the light intensity received by the photomultiplier. The instrument is often fairly compact, with the light spot on a small platform which takes the sample negative, and a head which is brought down onto the sample with a lever movement. This head contains colour filters, for use in COLORIMETRY, and reference densities.

The light bulb and electronics are carefully manufactured so that they give as near constant readings as possible. There are bound to be small variations, however, so a reference sample of known density has to be measured frequently and

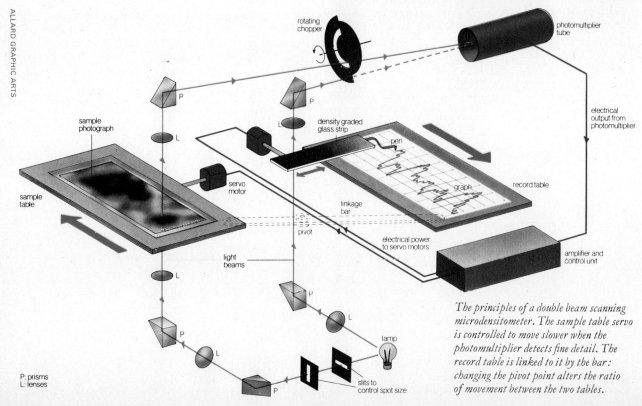

rotating chopper

photomultiplier tube

P

P

electrical output from photomultiplier

sample photograph

density graded glass strip

pen

L

L

servo motor

record table

graph

sample table

linkage bar

pivot

amplifier and control unit

electrical power to servo motors

light beams

L

P

L

P

L

lamp

P

slits to control spot size

P: prisms
L: lenses

The principles of a double beam scanning microdensitometer. The sample table servo is controlled to move slower when the photomultiplier detects fine detail. The record table is linked to it by the bar: changing the pivot point alters the ratio of movement between the two tables.

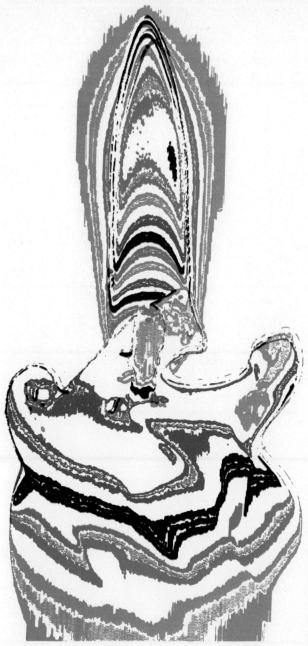

the reading of the meter adjusted to give the correct value. The densitometer is then ready for use.

An important adaptation of this principle is the *scanning microdensitometer*. This uses a very small spot of light, of diameter, say, 50 micrometres (0.05 mm) which is of the same order of size as the detail on a photographic negative. The sample is moved slowly across the spot, so that a continuous record of the density variations is obtained. This is not displayed on a meter, but instead a SERVO-MECHANISM moves a pen across a graph. The graph paper is moved simultaneously with the sample so that a continuous graph of the density across the negative is drawn.

It is not possible with this system to make constant corrections for the light and photomultiplier output, so a slightly different method is used. The light is split into two beams, one of which is passed through the sample while the other passes through a glass strip which is graded in density—clear at one end and dense at the other. The glass strip is moved by the same servo-mechanism that operates the pen, and the photomultiplier output is designed to equalize the intensities of the two beams—so moving the pen to correspond to the sample density.

Another variation is the *isophotometer*. This also gives a record of the density variations along a line of the sample, but a three pen system is coded to give a sequence of coloured marks on the paper, along one straight line, as the density varies. A certain known change in density is then represented by a colour change. The whole area of the photograph, rather than a single line, is scanned in a raster pattern similar to the lines on a TV screen. Eventually a contour map of the photograph is built up, the lines of constant colour linking points of equal density. This makes it possible to distinguish structures on the photograph which would otherwise be difficult to see.

DENSITY (see specific gravity)

Top left: this densitometer is designed to make sure that workers in an atomic research establishment do not receive a harmful radiation dose. They wear film badges which are then processed and the amount of blackening caused by radiation measured on this machine.

Above: a four colour trace of a burning candle, made using an isophotometer. A black and white photograph of the candle is scanned on a standard microdensitometer, and the electrical output fed into an electronic system which converts the signals into pen movements. This system makes it possible to gain much more information from a scientific photograph than can be shown on a straight print.

Right: a spot densitometer, used for making single density readings. The sample is placed at the centre of the illuminated platform, and the reading head brought down on it. The density is shown digitally.

DENTISTRY

Dentistry is the part of medicine and surgery which is concerned with the mouth cavity, the teeth, the bones of the jaws and the overlying soft tissues, together with the prevention, diagnosis and treatment of diseases of these parts.

The function and appearance of the mouth, and particularly the teeth, play an important role in every individual's daily life. When eating, the mouth is used in the first stage of digestion to taste, chew, moisten and swallow food. In communication, the mouth and teeth act in the articulation of speech and also contribute extensively to the general appearance of the face and to the silent facial signals which express the emotions, such as smiling or grimacing. In dental disease these important activities are impaired and the quality of life is affected to some degree. Discoloured, irregular or decaying front teeth and unhealthy gums present an unsightly feature to others while loss of teeth, unless they can be quickly and adequately replaced, make the subject feel and look older, affect his speech and may restrict his diet to soft foods. In addition, the mouth and teeth are well supplied with nerve endings and are thus extremely sensitive.

History Toothache has always been one of the worst discomforts of mankind and many attempts have been made to deal with dental decay, toothache and loss of teeth.

The Egyptians in 4000 BC used an assortment of medicaments and the Chinese in 2000 BC treated dental complaints with herbs and acupuncture. The ancient Greeks in the 5th century BC described the operation of dental extraction, and the Romans in the 1st century AD carried out extractions, fillings and constructed false teeth. When the Roman Empire declined there was a rapid deterioration of rational, scientific thought and the treatment of disease was neglected. For centuries dentistry is Europe seems to have been almost totally confined to the extraction of teeth.

By the 14th century in England the barber-surgeons were the acknowledged experts not only in the arts of shaving, hair cutting and wig making but also in bleeding and tooth-drawing. Their red and white striped barber's poles advertised that they were prepared to bleed the sick and were often festooned with strings of successfully extracted teeth to encourage toothache sufferers to seek their aid.

It was not until the 18th century that medicine and surgery were again influenced by a revival of scientific spirit, and the advance of dentistry has proceeded steadily ever since.

Anaesthetics In 1844-1846, in America, Horace Wells and W T G Morton pioneered the use of general anaesthesia, produced by nitrous oxide or ether, for dental extractions. On 19 December 1846, James Robinson, a London dentist, was the first man in Britain to carry out an operation under general anaesthesia when he removed a tooth while his patient slept after inhaling ether vapour. This technique, evolved for dentistry, introduced a safe method of producing temporary unconsciousness with complete insensitivity to the pain of an operation, which was to revolutionize the whole practice of surgery.

The next advance is painless dentistry came with the development of local anaesthesia. The hypodermic syringe and hollow needle had been invented in 1845 but the first clinical demonstration of local anaesthesia was given by Halsted in 1884, using an intradermal (within the skin) injection of cocaine to render an area of the body insensitive to pain during surgery while the patient remained fully conscious.

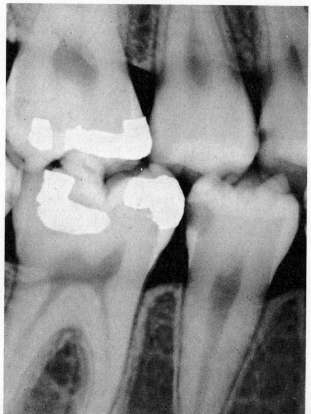

Above: The Country Tooth Drawer, an old drawing showing a Doctor Yankum at work. Tooth trouble seems to have been the source of some amusement. By contrast, the photo at right is an X-ray showing fillings in the teeth. The modern dentist can read an X-ray to differentiate between old fillings, new caries, any fillings which need repair, and any other abnormalities which may appear, instead of just pulling out teeth, as in the bad old days.

MARY EVANS PICTURE LIBRARY

FREDERICK ROTHERY

Other important discoveries After these major discoveries in pain control, the treatment of dental disease and the development of techniques to restore the teeth advanced rapidly. Electricity was used to speed up the dental DRILL and to provide better illumination in the dental surgery. The discovery of antiseptics, X-rays, antibiotics, plastics and progress in metallurgy, materials and drugs have all played a part in the advancement of modern dentistry.

The profession of dental surgery has now expanded into a widely based scientific subject and embraces matters far removed from just the techniques of treatment of dental decay and gum diseases.

Structure of teeth Healthy teeth are hard, mineralized structures which are held by strong fibres in sockets in the bone of the upper and lower jaws. The root is the part of the tooth attached to the jaw and the crown is the visible portion.

Teeth are composed of four different tissues: enamel, dentine, pulp and cementum. *Enamel* is the highly mineralized, insensitive outer covering of the crown and the hardest tissue in the body.

Dentine, which forms the bulk of the tooth, is a sensitive tissue receiving its nourishment from a fluid which permeates the dentine structure through *tubules.* This fluid is derived from the pulp cavity.

Pulp is the 'nerve' of the tooth and is situated in a chamber in the dentine extending down into the root end. Through the roots, blood and nerve fibres are supplied to the pulp.

Cementum, which covers the outside of the roots, is a bone-like substance which provides attachment for the fibres of the supporting *periodontal membrane.* It is this membrane which

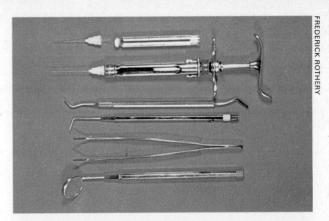

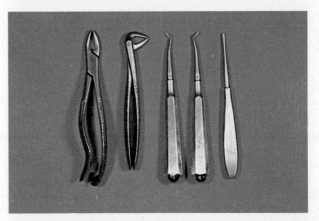

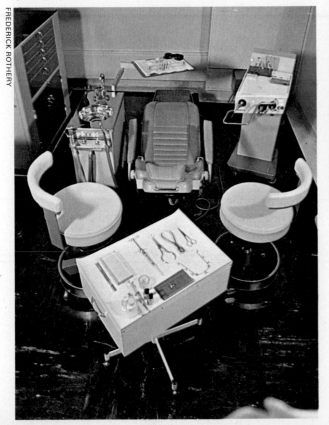

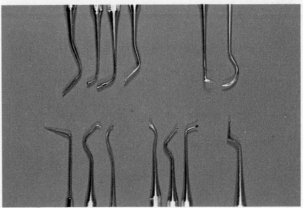

Left: a modern dental surgery. The layout of the furniture and equipment has to be such that all of the tools which might be needed are within reach. A dental assistant is also necessary, for example to mix the material used for filling cavities, which must be mixed and used quickly before it hardens.

Above: three photographs of selections of dental tools. The top picture shows a hypodermic syringe used to inject anaesthetics. The momentary sting from the needle is usually the only discomfort the patient experiences in modern dentistry. Disposable needles are available, so that the needle being used is always sterile and sharp. At the bottom of the top picture is a mirror which the dentist uses to see in difficult places. In the centre picture are extracting tools, and the rest of the tools are various kinds of special-purpose picks and excavators.

holds the tooth in the bone socket. The gingiva or 'gum' surrounds the neck of the tooth and prevents infection from penetrating between the tooth and the bony socket.

Orthodontics

The bone of the jaw supporting the teeth is a living substance that reacts to and is moulded by the forces acting upon it from using the teeth and general muscular stresses. Any abnormal forces lead to gradual changes in teeth positions and irregularities can occur. The prevention and correction of such irregularities is the branch of dentistry called *Orthodontics*.

In orthodontic treatment, the 'plastic' quality of the surrounding bone structure is exploited to reshape the jaw and reposition the teeth, through the application of a continuous gentle pressure. Stainless steel springs, elastic bands and screw fixtures are used to do this. Where there is overcrowding of the teeth, some may have to be extracted to make space for the correct repositioning of the rest.

Tooth decay

Dental caries or 'tooth decay' is the most universally prevalent disease affecting teeth. It is found particularly in children and young people who eat a diet rich in sugars and other highly refined carbohydrates.

When food debris is allowed to collect undisturbed on the tooth surfaces it quickly forms an inherent scum or dental plaque filled with multiplying bacteria which break down sugars and produce a strong acid which attacks the enamel. After a period of time the enamel disintegrates and other bacteria invade the unprotected dentine. If left undisturbed, the infection will finally reach the pulp as the dentine is softened and destroyed—leading to toothache.

Without treatment, the pulp (and nerve endings) are killed —which leads to a temporary relief from pain—but the infection continues down the root causing pain and swelling of the jaw. This is the dental abscess or 'gum boil'.

Treatment

When teeth are damaged by dental caries, the infected area can be removed and the resulting cavity filled with an amalgam (a mercury based alloy). The extent of damage is not always visible, however, and X-rays are taken of the teeth to show the internal damage. This technique, known as *dental radiography,* is frequently used in the examination of teeth and jaws for the presence of disease.

A piece of photographic film, protected from light and moisture by a suitable packet, is held in the mouth behind the teeth and a beam of X-rays aimed at it from outside. The rays pass through the teeth, supporting bone and soft tissues, and throw a varying 'shadow' upon the film. When the film is developed—using normal photographic methods—it will show details in and around the teeth that cannot be seen by the naked eye.

Once the extent of the damage has been determined, the correct treatment can be applied. Firstly, the tooth can be rendered insensitive with a local anaesthetic injection. Then the infected and softened parts of the tooth are removed. This can be done using either a dental drill or hand held instruments such as the dental excavator. The cavity is extended to the desired outline so that the filling can be fixed firmly. The walls are smoothed, cleaned with warm water, dried with air and a protective cement lining inserted. Antiseptics are rarely used at this point because they lead to more damage and irritation than they prevent. Often zinc phosphate cement is used for the lining; it is made by mixing a liquid and powder together in the required proportions and then moulded into the cavity to provide the final shape for the

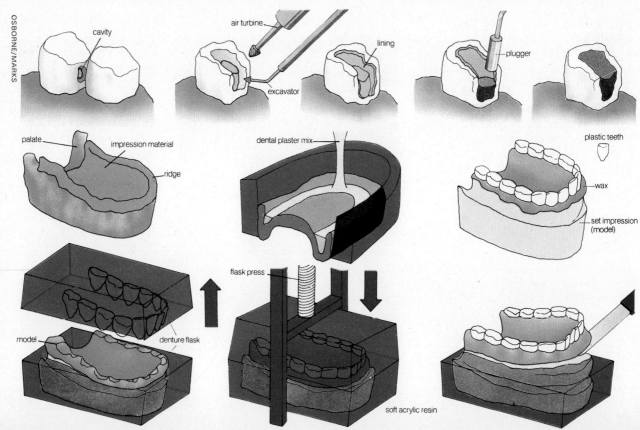

OSBORNE/MARKS

cavity · air turbine · lining · plugger · excavator

palate · impression material · ridge · dental plaster mix · plastic teeth · wax · set impression (model)

model · denture flask · flask press · soft acrylic resin

amalgam. This cement acts as an insulating lining to protect the tooth interior, for example, from heat which can easily pass through the amalgam.

Dental amalgams An amalgam is composed of a mixture of one or more metals with mercury. The alloy is made by combining finely ground particles of the constituent metals —usually at least 65% silver and 25% tin together with copper and zinc, with a measured amount of mercury. The resulting amalgam is at first soft and plastic enough to be packed into the prepared cavity and contoured to shape before it sets. When hard, it has an impervious crystalline structure, resistant to wear and chemical effects of mouth fluids. Dental amalgam alloys of this type have been developed so that they do not alter in size as they harden. Contraction could lead to a loose filling and expansion to an overstressed cavity.

When the amalgam is hard—after a few minutes—it is carved to restore the lost tooth shape and 24 hours later it can be polished with rotary brushes.

Crowning and artificial teeth Where there is extensive loss of tooth substance, restoration can be made using a 'cap' or crown. This can be complete or partial replacement for the crown of the tooth. Materials commonly used are gold or CERAMICS such as porcelain. These are constructed from accurate impressions of the damaged tooth, which has been ground down to a peg shape during preparation. Gold can be easily cast to the required shape, but being a soft metal, it is alloyed with other metals to make it harder and more resistant to wear. Porcelain jacket crowns are prepared by heating the ceramic material in a furnace on a platinum foil base. The foil is then removed and the crown is cemented into place using zinc phosphate or other cements.

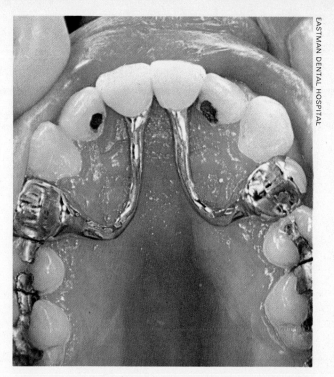

Above: if crowns or false teeth need support from surrounding teeth in order to stay in place properly, there are a variety of ways of designing connections or supports according to the problem. If it bridges a gap, it is called bridgework.

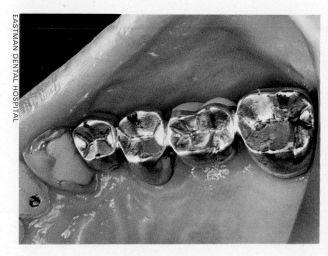

Above: a bridge of gold crowns and false teeth. When teeth are badly decayed or broken, crowns are made to restore the shape. They are cemented in place, and can be made of porcelain for natural appearance.

Left: amalgam restoration. The cavity and surrounding material is removed completely with a drill or dental excavator, lined and then plugged with a mixture of dental amalgam.
Denture construction: plastic teeth are set into wax on a plaster model of the palate and enclosed in a dental flask containing more plaster. On reopening, the teeth and model are held in the plaster. Soft acrylic resin is pressed between the two parts and heated to 'cure' it. The completed denture is removed and polished.

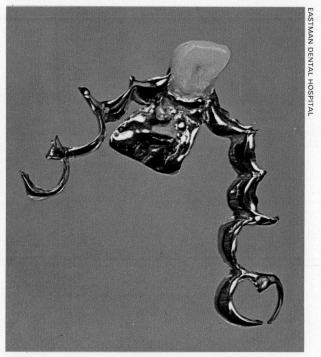

Above: the support necessary for this one false tooth is precisely and ingeniously designed. The hook-shaped parts on each end clip onto other teeth. The large mass directly behind the false tooth fits into the mouth and holds the tooth at the right angle.

EASTMAN DENTAL HOSPITAL

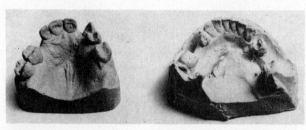

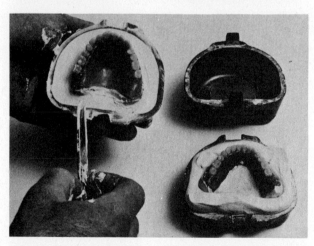

These pictures illustrate some of the steps in making dentures. First the dentist takes an impression of the gums by pressing a small tray of soft plastic material against them. The top picture above shows the initial impressions being filled with Kaffir plaster to make a model of the gums. In the centre picture are a pair of models; the one on the left is trimmed. (This patient still had some teeth.) Models like these are then used to make a set of dentures out of wax for a trial fitting in the mouth of the patient. When a satisfactory fitting has been obtained, the wax model is used to make a mould for the actual dentures, which may be made of plastic or metal. In the lower picture, wax models are being invested with dental plaster.

When the teeth are so badly damaged or infected that they have to be extracted, replacement false teeth or dentures can be fitted. These can be replaced individually or in groups. When necessary, a fixed 'bridge' can be provided which secures the tooth or teeth to adjacent natural ones for support.

Where many or all the teeth have been lost, dentures can be fitted where the artificial teeth are mounted on a plate moulded to the contours of upper or lower gum ridges. To do this, impressions of the jaws are taken by pressing a soft material, held in a metal tray, over the teeth and gum ridges. After a few moments the material sets, and the tray and its contents are removed. The impression in the material is an accurate record of the jaw shape. A creamy mix of dental plaster is poured into the impression and when it sets forms a replica, or model, of the mouth. From this the size of the replacement teeth can be determined and also the size of the supporting plates. Materials commonly used in dentures include metals, such as stainless steel and gold, and plastics, such as methyl methacrylate (an acrylic material similar to 'Perspex' and 'Plexiglas').

Diseases of the gums Gingivitis and periodontal disease are diseases of the gums and supporting structure of the teeth. Although less dramatic than dental caries they are responsible for the loss of many teeth in people over 35. The first stages are, however, detectable in adolescence.

Inflammation of the gums may be due to general ill health (requiring medical attention) but the most common factor is poor oral hygiene. Again, sugars and bacteria build up between the teeth—forming a *plaque*—which cause irritation of the gums leading to swelling and bleeding. This gives rise to the 'pink toothbrush' when brushing the teeth.

If this first stage is neglected, a breach is made between the tooth and the socket and hard 'tartar' or calculus builds up in the pocket so formed. A slow and insidious but often painless breakdown of the supporting structures commences and the teeth inevitably loosen unless treatment is sought in time.

Preventive dentistry Preventive dentistry is the science and practice of measures to prevent the onset of dental disease. The traditional preoccupation of dentistry was with the practical problems of repair but although this remains important, much can now be done to eliminate the causes of dental disorders.

The enamel of the teeth will be much stronger and more acid resistant if an adequate amount of the trace element fluorine is available in the diet during the period of teeth formation before they erupt in the mouth. Water in some areas already contains one part per million of fluorine, but where the water is deficient in this element, a fluoride preparation can be added. When the teeth have erupted into the mouth, fluoride solutions, gels and varnishes can be applied directly onto the enamel, although this cannot provide the 'defence in depth' effect of pre-natal fluorinated water consumption.

Harmful bacteriological (plaque forming) activity in the mouth can be reduced by avoiding sweet foods. But where plaque has formed, thorough cleaning using a toothbrush or dental floss (a waxed thread) used between the teeth is required. Soft wooden sticks are also useful for removing foodstuffs which have collected between the teeth.

The vulnerable crevices and pits found in normal teeth surfaces can be further protected from plaque formations by sealing them with a hard, transparent plastic before dental decay sets in.

DERAILLEUR GEAR

The two main forms of gearing for bicycles are the *derailleur* type and the enclosed hub gear or EPICYCLIC GEAR. The first modern form of derailleur appeared in France in 1909, although various designs had been tried since about 1899. The derailleur is a light, positive, and reliable mechanism, using interchangeable sets of between two and six sprockets of different diameters screwed onto a common freewheel. There also may be up to three chainwheels mounted side by side on the crank spindle. The gearchange mechanism is fixed to the frame next to the rear wheel spindle and the freewheel set. The main arm of the changer extends downwards and slightly forwards, carrying an S-shaped cage containing two small guide sprockets or wheels. The chain passes over one of the freewheel sprockets and down through the cage, which is spring loaded towards the rear to maintain chain tension and also towards the wheel to assist the gearchange operation.

The gearchange is effected by moving the chain from one sprocket to another. The gearlever is connected by a cable to the changer mechanism; to change to a higher ratio the cable pulls the cage outwards against the action of the spring and the chain is shifted to a smaller sprocket. To change to a lower gear the cage is allowed to move inwards under the action of the spring and move the chain to a larger sprocket. A friction clamp prevents the gearlever from slipping, and this maintains the tension in the cable, holding the cage in the required position.

Where more than one chainwheel is fitted, the chain passes through a cage mounted on the frame above the crank spindle. When the cage is moved sideways, by a cable or by a rod mounted on the frame, the chain is transferred from one chainwheel to another. Derailleur gears (named from the French word meaning 'derail') are used mainly on lightweight sports and touring cycles.

RALEIGH

Above: a modern derailleur gear. Chains used with derailleurs are fully riveted, because the spring clip on the connecting link of an ordinary chain will jam in the mechanism or be forced off the chain.

Below: the derailleur gear mechanism. Depression of the small hand lever on the frame increases the tension in the cable and moves the lever carrying the jockey pulley over the range of sprockets each representing a gear. In the system illustrated there is also a second chain wheel which in combination with the 5 rear sprockets gives a range of ten possible gear ratios.

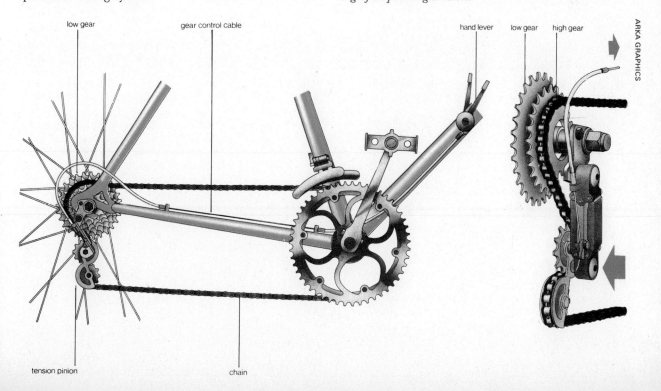

ARKA GRAPHICS

low gear   gear control cable   hand lever   low gear   high gear

tension pinion   chain

DESALINATION

Desalination [desalinization] is the process of converting sea water, which contains 35,000 parts per million (ppm) of salt, or brackish water, containing 5000 to 10,000 ppm of salt, to fresh water suitable for human consumption, household and industrial requirements. The salt in drinking water should not normally exceed 500 ppm and where natural supplies of water of this quality are insufficient, desalination is the alternative to transporting fresh water over long distances by pipeline or tank vehicle.

Many types of evaporator have been used to produce fresh water by DISTILLATION, but they have proved costly and troublesome when used continuously on the large scale which is often required. At temperatures over 160°F (71°C), sea water and many brackish waters deposit *scale* (incrustation of insoluble chemical compounds, especially calcium and magnesium salts) which interferes with heat transfer. (Water normally boils at 212°F, 100°C, but by reducing the pressure it will boil at a lower temperature.) Hot sea water is also very corrosive. At low temperatures, however, it is difficult to recover the latent heat of water vapour (that is, the quantity of heat absorbed by the water in passing from the liquid to the vapour phase) by conventional multiple effect methods. In these the steam from one evaporator is used to heat another working at a lower temperature and pressure. At low operating temperatures, because of the small temperature differences

Right: equipment for studying freezing techniques for desalination of sea water. A refrigerant (butane) immiscible with sea water is used to freeze it. The small crystals formed are washed free of traces of salt and subsequently melted to provide fresh water.

Below: a flash chamber evaporator; the flashing can be seen as a foam of sea water and vapour. Water enters from a higher pressure chamber on the left and after flashing passes to lower pressure on the right.

available for heat transfer and the increasing volumes of vapour that have to be condensed to produce a gallon of fresh water, this method becomes increasingly inefficient. Furthermore, the total energy requirement will become very large if the latent heat is only used once.

Modern desalination processes try to avoid these difficulties either by using modified forms of low temperature distillation or by adopting non-distillation methods.

Flash distillation This process is now the most important method of desalinating sea water because it makes the utmost possible use of latent heat while working at temperatures low enough to avoid scaling and corrosion troubles. Hot sea water passes into an area where the pressure is reduced and some of it immediately evaporates. This instantaneous boiling and the generation of vapour without a heat supply is known as *flashing*.

Distillation takes place and the hot sea water is cooled in the process. Further flash steam can be released at a lower pressure and temperature in another stage, and so on in a series of stages.

A typical flash distillation plant consists of a series of chambers, each operating at a lower temperature than the previous one, and where the condensing coils are banks of finned tubes. The initial heat input can be low pressure steam which has already done useful work, for instance in a back pressure steam turbine. The heated brine flows from one chamber to the next, the water vapour generated passing through moisture separators to remove any entrained (carried along) brine droplets.

The vapour is then condensed, the fresh water distillate falling into collecting trays. The water is run off from these trays and goes to bulk storage. As the brine passes from chamber to chamber it becomes progressively cooler. It is this cooled brine that is pumped back through the condenser tubes. As it passes from one stage to another more heat is absorbed from the steam and it becomes hotter and hotter. By the time it reaches the heat input unit only a small amount of heat is required to raise it to the correct temperature for recycling through the chambers.

Some very large plants of this type have now been built in arid localities near the sea. One near Tijuana, on the Mexican coast, was completed in 1970 and produces 27 million litres (6 million UK, 7 million US gallons) per day of fresh water from sea water.

Vapour compression evaporation This method may also be referred to as vapour compression distillation. Like any other gas, the temperature of steam can be raised by compression. If the compressed steam is then condensed at the higher pressure, its latent heat can be returned to the boiling liquid it came from. This principle is used in the vapour compression desalinator, where the energy is supplied not as heat but rather as mechanical work. In this process hot sea water is introduced into an evaporator and the steam produced is drawn off and compressed, which raises its temperature as well as its pressure. This steam is then fed into another part of the evaporator where it condenses into fresh water. As it condenses, however, it heats up the sea water providing more evaporation. The condensed fresh water is quite warm and on its way to storage it is passed through a heat exchanger, where the heat extracted is used to heat up the incoming sea water supply.

Below centre: a multi-stage flash distillation plant, which is one of six each producing a total of nine million litres of fresh water from sea water per day for the Government of Abu Dhabi.

Below: reverse osmosis plant trials for desalination. The salt water is forced under pressure against a semi-permeable membrane in the form of a series of thin long tubes. The process is currently economic only for low salinity or brackish water.

These vapour compression plants can be made very compact, and packaged units mounted on skids are now made for temporary supplies in the USA. The small temperature difference available for heat transfer makes it necessary to avoid waters which deposit scale, and to have a very efficient means of removing non-condensable gases from the steam side of the condenser. A large fixed distillation plant has been built at Roswell, New Mexico, USA.

Solar distillation This is a very cheap and simple method, but its usefulness is limited to sub-tropical regions because very large water areas are needed at higher latitudes. Sea water is placed in a shallow tray with an insulated black lining and covered by a sloping roof of glass or transparent plastic. Sunlight passing through the glass is absorbed by the black lining and re-emitted as infra-red radiation (heat) which warms the water, causing it to evaporate and condense on the cooler under-surface of the glass. This runs down the glass into collecting troughs. The sea water in the trays is changed periodically; otherwise it begins to deposit solids. Experience has shown that 10 square feet (1 m²) of water surface is necessary to produce 4.5 litres of drinking water each day in latitude 37°. Several successful installations have been built on arid Greek islands, notably on Simi, near Rhodes.

Freezing As the latent heat of melting ice is much less than the latent heat of steam, freezing appears to be an excellent method of obtaining fresh water because the ice which forms on salt water melts to give fresh water. Unfortunately serious effluent problems arise because a gallon of strong brine, twice as salty as sea water, has to be discarded for each gallon of fresh water produced. Operating costs have proved higher than for evaporation processes and large scale development of this method is unlikely.

Reverse osmosis Pure water diffuses through a *semi-*

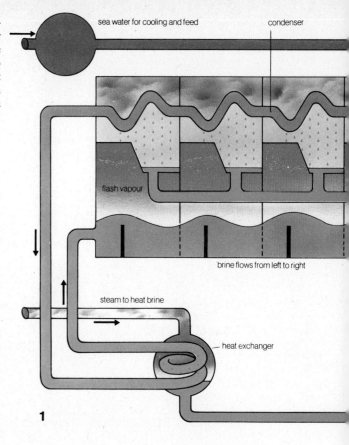

1

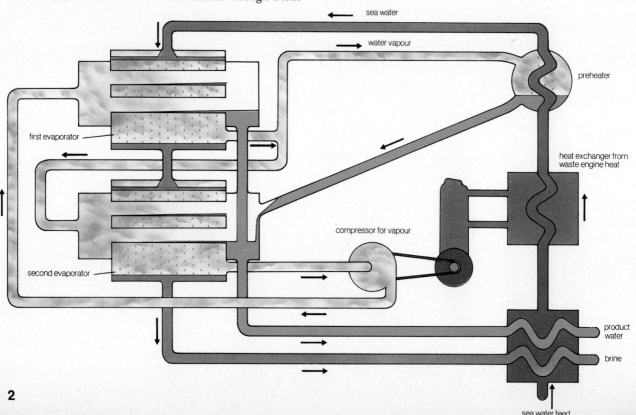

2

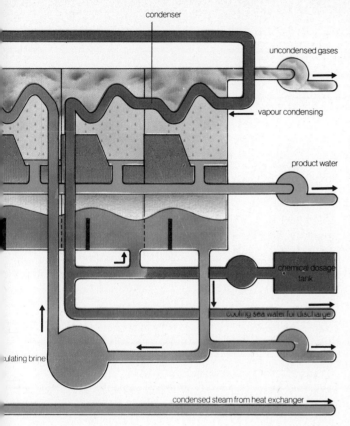

condenser

uncondensed gases

vapour condensing

product water

chemical dosage tank

cooling sea water for discharge

circulating brine

condensed steam from heat exchanger

permeable membrane (one that allows passage of solvent but not dissolved substances) into a salt solution under the driving force of OSMOTIC PRESSURE when there is the same hydrostatic pressure on each side of the membrane. When the pressure on the salt side exceeds that on the fresh side by more than the osmotic pressure for that particular combination of solution and membrane, fresh water is driven out of the salt solution by reverse osmosis. The membrane is usually cellulose acetate held on a porous support with a pressure of 600 psi (40 bar), or more, on the inside. There have been many problems with membrane breakages, and research is being carried out to find a stronger membrane, such as a synthetic polymer. Although the pressures required are rather high and increase with salt content, these problems are being overcome.

Electrodialysis When an electric current is passed through an electrolyte (conductive fluid), the cations (positively charged IONS) migrate towards the cathode (negative terminal) and the anions (negative ions) towards the anode (positive terminal). When a series of alternate cation and anion-permeable membranes is placed between two electrodes in a saline solution and a current is passed through the solution, the cations (Na^+) and anions (Cl^-) collect in different compartments. Eventually they become filled alternately with fresh water and stronger salt solution. The consumption of electricity depends on the amount of salt to be removed, and the method is limited in practice to brackish waters containing less than 10,000 ppm of salt. Electrodialysis plants with outputs up to $2\frac{1}{4}$ million litres (500,000 UK, 600,000 US gallons) per day are now used for treating brackish waters in the United States.

DETECTORS, PARTICLE (see particle detector)

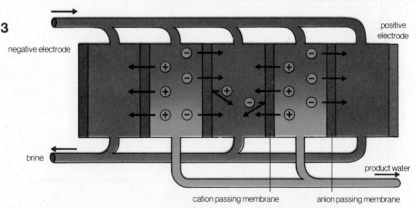

3

negative electrode

positive electrode

brine

product water

cation passing membrane

anion passing membrane

DIAGRAM

Examples of desalination systems. 1 multi-stage flash distillation. In arid regions, such as Kuwait, these plants run continuously. 2 vapour compression evaporation. This is more suitable for smaller units, up to about 23 million litres per day. 3 electrodialysis —a commercial plant may have up to 300 of these cells. 4 reverse osmosis—a simple direct way to purify water. Such units have a fairly low output, about 23,000 litres per day.

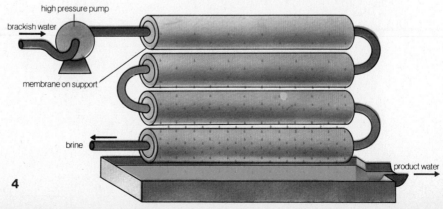

high pressure pump

brackish water

membrane on support

brine

product water

4

DETECTOR VAN

A detector van is a vehicle equipped with specialized apparatus for detecting and locating unlicenced TELEVISION RECEIVERS while they are being used. Such vans are operated by authorities in many countries—in Britain, by the Post Office Corporation. The detector van crew know which dwellings are covered by a valid TV receiver licence and concentrate on the remainder. With their equipment they can determine accurately the direction and distance, and in some circumstances, the floor and even the room where a TV set is being operated.

Detection Every domestic TV receiver contains an oscillator circuit which generates waveforms for both the sound and vision circuitry. This emits ELECTROMAGNETIC RADIATION (radio waves) with a characteristic frequency that is not found in other appliances commonly used in the home. The van is equipped with directional AERIALS, which sense this radiation, AMPLIFIERS for amplifying the weak signals received, and recording apparatus.

Locating the source of radiation Two types of aerial system may be used. One works on the principle of the direction finding loop or *goniometer*, used widely in NAVIGATION. Another more recent system has two directional aerials, both pointing in the same direction, arranged as an INTERFEROMETER. This technique is widely used in RADIO ASTRONOMY to make very detailed maps of distant radio sources.

The combined signals of the two aerials have a distinctive reception pattern with one particularly strong *lobe* or area of sensitivity. The two aerials are fixed when in use, pointing at right angles to the direction of motion of the van, so that as the van travels along the road the lobe sweeps the buildings. The signals detected are then amplified.

The output from the amplifier is displayed on two similar OSCILLOSCOPE tubes, one of which is viewed by the operator, while the other can be photographed using a POLAROID CAMERA. As the vehicle moves, a linkage from the van's speedometer causes a spot to sweep across the tube faces, in step with the aerials scanning the buildings. The operator can add marker lines as the van passes the edges of buildings.

As the van moves along the street, the images of the spot and markers are stored by a time exposure on the Polaroid film. On development, which takes seconds, the result is a photograph showing a pattern of blips, corresponding to the aerial response to the TV set, and marker lines. These are then measured directly to pinpoint the exact location of the TV receiver.

Depending on the national laws, the van crew may not have right of access to the house or wherever the set is operating. Under these circumstances the only evidence is from the detector van. This presents problems at the end of a cul-de-sac, for example, where the van cannot drive past the source of the signal. In a high-rise office or block of flats, too, it is often difficult to pick out the correct floor.

Above right: a British detector van, with the interferometer pair of aerials on top. These are 'logarithmic spirals', which combine good directionality with sensitivity to a wide range of frequencies.

Right: the control desk inside the van. Before the system can be used, it has to be tuned in to the signals from the suspect receiver, as shown here. They are different for each TV channel.

DETERGENT manufacture

The word detergent has become a loose description for both the traditional SOAP and the newer non-soapy synthetic materials. There are different kinds of detergent products ranging from simple tablets and flakes to complex powders and liquids, formulated to cope with various washing systems.

When washing skin, for example, a dense lather is needed to trap and remove any dirt, so the product must produce a good lather without becoming mushy in use. In addition it should not interact adversely with the skin. A more complex product, however, is that needed for washing fabrics. It must eliminate calcium and other substances present in natural water, which would otherwise hinder the removal of dirt. Furthermore the dirt must be removed efficiently with a minimum of mechanical force and be kept in suspension so that it cannot become redeposited on the fabric. Stains must be removed and off-colour caused by aging counteracted. But in carrying out all these functions the product must not harm the fabric.

It is also important that detergents are biodegradable—capable of being broken down naturally by bacteria after use. Soap is naturally so, but non-soapy detergents must be designed to be so as well, to prevent pollution.

Detergent constituents and action The key to all detergent action is the *surfactant*, so called because it modifies the surface quality of the water by weakening the forces between water molecules. In simple terms, this helps the water to more readily wet the object being washed. This is because of the character of the surfactant molecules which, though far too small to be observed, are known to contain a 'water-loving' head, which anchors in the surface, attached

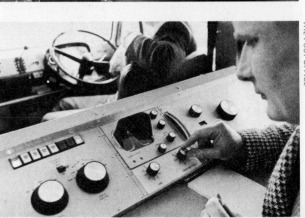

to a 'water-hating' tail that is forced to protrude from the surface, so breaking the strong electrostatic forces between the water molecules in the surface. There are two kinds of surfactant: soap, made from fats, and non-soapy detergents (NSD), made mostly nowadays from petroleum by-products, such as alkylaryl sulphonate. NSD itself is not so good a detergent as soap. For one thing, it does not lather so well. Finding out why has led not only to a better understanding of the mechanisms of dirt removal but also to all round improvement in detergent products. For example, to meet the need for minimal lather in front-loading washing machines a non-lathering NSD had to be developed—alkyl phenol polyethylene oxide is the one most widely used. Conversely, to improve the lathering power of a general purpose NSD product a *lather booster* must be incorporated. This has a molecular structure similar to that of a surfactant and is in competition with it for a place in the surface.

Most products contain anything up to a dozen or so constituents, each with a specific purpose, though not every one is involved in detergent action. Washing powders, for example, will contain an anti-corrosion agent to protect the bowls of washing machines. Tablets and flakes are the only products that depend substantially on surfactant alone. Both are based on soap, and both rely for their product properties on the selection and treatment of the fats used for conversion to soap, and on the subsequent processing of the soap. In all other products detergent action is shared for the most part by the surfactant and a *builder*, so named because it builds up the surfactant into a more complete detergent. The usual builder is sodium tripolyphosphate. Broadly speaking the surfactant, which may be either soap or NSD, takes care of

fatty dirt, and the builder of solid particulate dirt, but there is some mutual support.

For fabric washing the two are required in roughly equal proportions. For dish washing, where there is little mineral dirt, the surfactant predominates. For hard surface cleaning the proportions are reversed.

Fatty dirt is removed and dispersed in the wash liquor as minute negatively charged globules, and solid dirt as entrapped particles in negatively charged molecular cages, which are formed by compounds in the cleaning product. To prevent their redeposition on fabric it is given a repulsive charge by including in the product multi-charged *anti-redeposition agents,* each preferentially attracted to a particular type of fabric. Stain removal is commonly dealt with by a *chemical bleach,* sodium perborate, which performs well at the elevated temperatures and in the alkaline environment of the wash liquor. Off-colour is corrected by an *optical brightener,* a fluorescent material designed to adhere well to fabric and emit a bluish white light. Enzymes, which act as catalysts in breaking down protein stains such as blood, may also be included in a detergent.

Washing powders need to contain *conditioners,* that is, substances that help to produce a readily pourable and easily dissolved product, without detracting from the detergent action. The most suitable for soap powders is a mixture of sodium silicate and sodium sulphate. Liquid products contain

Below: two forms of detergent attack. In both the dislodged grease or dirt is subsequently held in solution and prevented from redepositing on the fabric. Fats are often removed by a tube mechanism—the tubes resulting from liquid crystal formation at the surface of the fat.

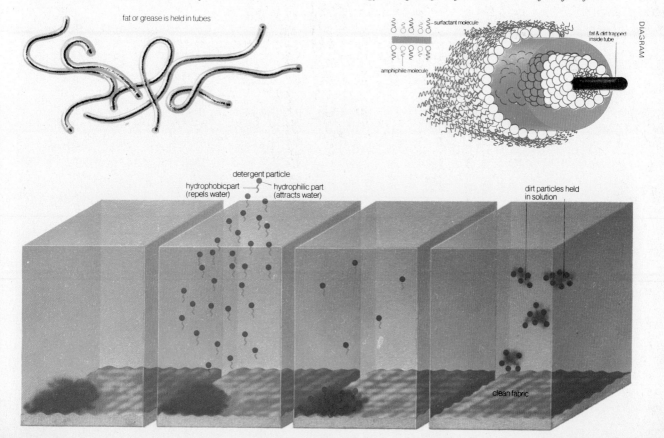

fat or grease is held in tubes

surfactant molecule

amphiphile molecule

fat & dirt trapped inside tube

DIAGRAM

detergent particle

hydrophobic part (repels water)

hydrophilic part (attracts water)

dirt particles held in solution

clean fabric

UNILEVER EDUCATIONAL PUBLICATIONS

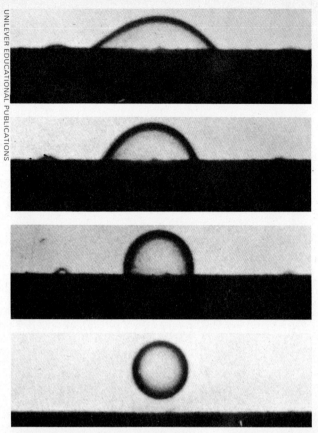

highly concentrated constituents that are mostly immiscible (unwilling to mix) with each other. A *hydrotrope,* that is, a solubilizing agent, such as sodium xylene sulphonate, is added to induce them to do so.

Manufacturing methods The manufacture of traditional soap is dealt with in detail elsewhere but is based on a mixture of fats which is fed proportionately with an alkali solution into a reaction vessel where it is saponified. After saponification the soap is purified and becomes known as 'neat' soap, and is ready for processing.

To make toilet tablets, the molten soap is cooled and flaked, dried to 96% soap mixed with trace constituents, such as perfume, triple milled between steel rollers, 'plodded' (compressed and extruded in bar form), cut and stamped. When soap flakes are required, the molten soap is cooled and flaked, mixed with trace constituents and milled to the required thickness between steel rollers which also cut it to shape.

For soap-based powders the molten soap is mixed with a builder and conditioners. The mixture is then heated and *spray-cooled* by extruding it at high pressure through nozzles at the head of a cooling chamber. It falls as granules through an uprising current of cool air on to a conveyer belt.

In the manufacture of NSD-based powders, a paste is formed of the NSD, lather booster (if required), builder and conditioners. The mixture is *spray-dried* by pumping it through nozzles into the headspace of a drying tower. The spray falls through an uprising current of hot air which dries the drops to hollow granules. The power is collected in the same way as soap powder, and heat-labile (unstable when heated) constituents are metered in as the powder travels along a conveyer belt.

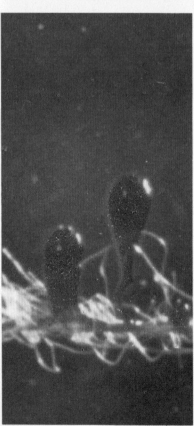

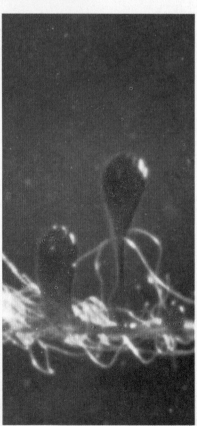

The manufacture of liquid NSD products is essentially simple. The process is one of obtaining a stable solution or suspension by mixing and no complex technical procedures are involved. The products are based on NSD which must be either near liquid or extremely soluble. Lather boosters of more than average solubility must also be used. Small quantities of many exotic detergent constituents find their way into these products, the formulation of which provides far greater complexity than does manufacture. The hydrotrope makes the various components miscible.

Left: a series of pictures showing the effect of detergent solution on fat or oil. The detergent causes the contact angle of the fat or oil with the fibre to increase, so that the fat eventually simply rolls up into a globule and becomes detached from the fabric. This reaction occurs more easily at high temperatures where the fat is more mobile.

Below: this is the same action as above and shows oil floating off a strand of fibre in a detergent solution. Although extremely effective, this action must be supplemented by some sort of chemical action to remove the more adherent constituents of the oil, as well as a certain amount of mechanical energy, such as tumbling in a washing machine.

Right: a micrograph showing the removal of fat from a fibre by a method other than rolling it up. This is known as mesomorphic phase formation, also called myelin tube formation because it was first observed when myelin nerve tissues were soaked in water. The tubes are the result of liquid crystal formation arising from the intermolecular attraction between the surfactant and the fat. This occurs at moderate temperatures where the fat is not so mobile, but is capable of forming some type of chemical bonding.

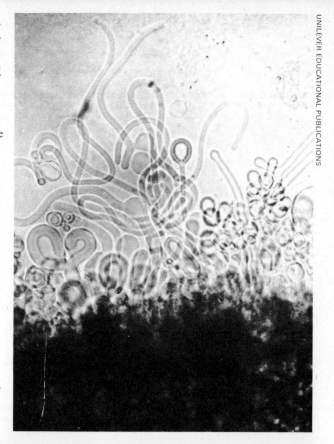

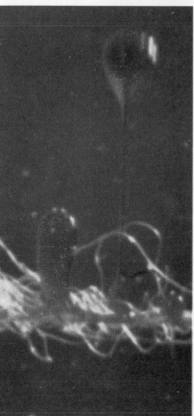
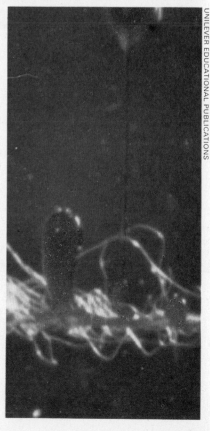

DETONATOR

Most EXPLOSIVES are difficult to explode and require a 'primer' or *initiating* device to start the explosive reaction in the main body of the explosive—this is the *detonator*.

In an explosion an enormous volume of gas and large quantities of heat are suddenly produced, but although the effect of this can be devastating the rate at which the reaction occurs is extremely slow compared with the process of detonation. Under the most favourable conditions a burning rate of about 1000 ft/sec (300 m/sec) would not be exceeded in an explosion.

In detonation, a chemical change takes place in the form of an extremely rapid burning which is propagated through the material at the speed of sound in that medium. This is never less than 6500 ft/sec (2 km/sec or 1.2 mile/sec) and can be as fast as 30,000 ft/sec (9 km/sec or 5.6 mile/sec). Owing to this high speed of propagation, there is an intense local disruption of the molecules of the material, which break up and then recombine to form gaseous products. It is either the heat produced in this process or the extremely disruptive high pressure shock wave (usually above 1,000,000 psi, 68,900 bar) that initiates the explosive reaction. Consequently, detonators are classified as *igniferous* (heat producing) or *disruptive* (producing shock waves), depending on which is the primary cause of the main explosion.

Fuzes may be incorporated in a detonator to control the time and distance of detonation. Sometimes an intermediary explosive is also required between the detonator and main explosive to boost the shock wave of detonation. This is necessary for 'insensitive' high explosives.

Historical development

In 1800, Edward Howard FRS discovered fulminate of mercury, $Hg(ONC)_2$, by adding mercury to nitric acid and mixing this with alcohol. The resulting dry crystals were found to be very sensitive to shock or friction and detonated violently when struck.

When high explosives were first used for filling shells, it was found difficult to set off the explosion. In 1864, however, Nobel discovered a way of using fulminate of mercury as an initiating agent. He used it as an detonator for nitroglycerine, but later his assistant, E A Brown, used it successfully with other explosives. With some explosives, such as wet gun-cotton (nitrocellulose) and TNT (trinitrotoluene), it was found necessary to interpose a boosting charge of dry gun-cotton to amplify the shock wave.

At the end of the 19th century it was appreciated that less sensitive explosives require detonators of greater power and a standard was prepared, which was eventually adopted internationally. The detonator filling was based on 80% mercury fulminate and 20% potassium chlorate. Ten different sizes were specified and designated as Trade Standards numbered 1 to 10. Trade Standard No 1 had a filling of 0.3 grammes and No 10 had 3.0 grammes.

During 1903, a lot of work was carried out at Spandau, near Berlin, by Will and Lenze on lead azide, PbN_6, as a detonator.

Below: a large current passes through the bridge wire of an electric detonator, lighting the surrounding explosive. Impact on the acid horn shatters the glass tube and acid enters the cell, setting up a current. In the typical impact detonator a firing pin hits the priming charge at a speed sufficient to ignite it.

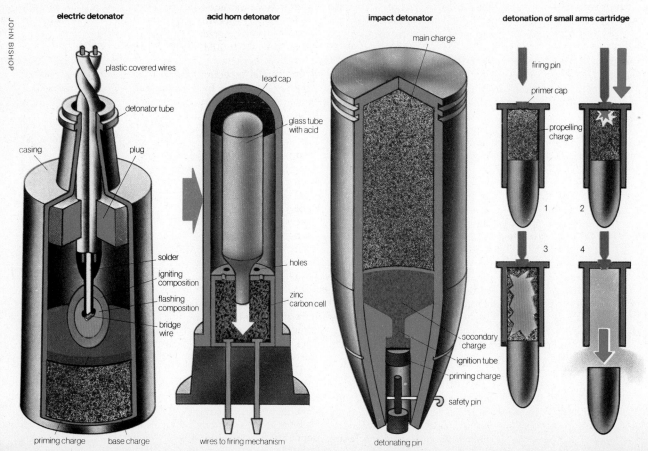

electric detonator

plastic covered wires
detonator tube
casing
plug
solder
igniting composition
flashing composition
bridge wire
priming charge   base charge

acid horn detonator

lead cap
glass tube with acid
holes
zinc carbon cell
wires to firing mechanism

impact detonator

main charge
secondary charge
ignition tube
priming charge
safety pin
detonating pin

detonation of small arms cartridge

firing pin
primer cap
propelling charge
1   2
3   4

JOHN BISHOP

Experiments ceased after a fatal accident but were resumed by others in 1907. In France, F Hyronimus suggested the use of lead azide in detonators in place of mercury fulminate, and this type of detonator was manufactured in most industrial countries in Europe before World War I. It was adopted in the USA some years later.

Lead azide was commonly used in commercial detonators in England but was not adopted as a military detonator filling until 1933 when the No 27 detonator—equivalent to the Trade Standard No 8—was introduced. The No 27 detonator was an aluminium tube 0.26 inches (6.4 mm) in diameter and 1.75 inches (44.5 mm) long. One end was open for the insertion of the initiating fuze and the other end was sealed. The working substance was a mixture of lead azide, powdered aluminium and lead styphate.

The detonators so far described were all initiated by using a slow burning type of fuze. As far back as 1866, Sir Frederick Abel had produced an electrically initiated detonator, but this technique was slow to replace the old type of fuze. Over the years, however, it has been successfully developed until now it is by far the most common type.

Classification of detonators

The parameters which determine the effectiveness and safety of a detonator are power, velocity of detonation, and sensitivity to detonation. Although developed towards the end of the last century, these parameters and the techniques for measuring them have remained substantially unchanged and are important in determining the choice of detonator for a particular explosive.

Power is determined using the Trauzl lead block test. In this, a given quantity of the detonating compound (usually ten grammes—0.35 ounces) is placed in a hole one inch (2.5 cm) in diameter and five inches (13 cm) deep in a lead block eight inches (20 cm) in diameter and eight inches (20 cm) high. The hole is firmly packed with sand. After electrical detonation the resulting volume of the cavity in the lead block is measured. This is compared with the volume produced from an equal quantity of picric acid (an explosive) fired under the same conditions. The volume produced by the picric acid is rated as '100' and the material under test is shown as a proportion of this figure.

The *velocity of detonation* is found using the Dautriche method. This produces an absolute velocity rating, but involves the use of PETN which has a known velocity of detonation—24,440 ft/sec which is 7450 m/sec or 4.65 mile/sec. PETN is the high explosive filling in *cordtex*—commonly used in detonating cords for industrial and military applications.

The *sensitivity rating* is based on how much of the material will explode when struck and in relationship to the force with which it is struck. Some extremely insensitive materials will only explode locally when struck and do not pass the explosive reaction through the whole material. This makes them inherently safe but useless detonators. At the other extreme, some materials will detonate totally at the least vibration. These are classified as highly sensitive and are inherently unstable and unsafe.

To determine the sensitivity (or insensitivity) rating, a weight is dropped from up to six different heights on to samples of the detonating material contained in caps. The volume of gas produced in each case is measured using a manometer. The results are plotted on a graph with the height of drop measured on the vertical axis and the percentage of detonation (determined by the amount of gas produced) along the horizontal axis. A similar curve obtained from caps containing picric acid is also plotted on this graph. The area under the test material curve is compared to the area under the standard picric acid curve (which is rated as '100'). The smaller the figure, the more sensitive is the compound.

Common applications The greatest use of detonators is in quarrying, coal mining and tunnelling. In all of these processes the explosives used are initiated by detonators. Although a safety fuze, which burns slowly, can be used with a plain detonator to provide a safe and easy means of initiating high explosives, it is far more convenient to employ electric shot firing using either instantaneous or delay detonators. There are two main methods: exploder (or blasting machine) firing and an exploder which works off the electricity mains. In coal mines in Britain and the USA it is illegal to fire shots except with approved exploders.

Detonator materials have few applications other than as initiating devices. There is, however, one interesting application which demonstrates the power of such materials although it is seldom used. To fell a tree or telegraph pole, a length of cordtex is wrapped around the trunk and one end is ignited. The shock wave travels rapidly around the trunk and with such force that it cuts the object in two.

DEUTERIUM AND DEUTERON (see Isotope)

DEWAR, Sir James (1842-1923)

Sir James Dewar, famous for the invention of the vacuum-insulated flask [Thermos bottle], was a pioneer in low-temperature research. The son of a Scottish wine shipper, he was born at Kincardine-on-Forth on 20 September 1842. A prolonged bout of rheumatic fever caused his schooling to be scanty, but he graduated to Edinburgh University in 1858 where he studied under Lyon Playfair (1818-1898), professor of chemistry.

In 1869 he became lecturer in chemistry at the Royal Veterinary College. In 1875, however, he moved to Cambridge on his appointment to the Jacksonian Professorship of natural experimental philosophy, and in 1877 he became Fullerian Professor of chemistry at the Royal Institution in London. He held both posts until his death, although nearly all his important work was conducted with the superior facilities at the Royal Institution, where many of his contemporaries were invited to spend convivial evenings in his rooms.

Dewar's early papers, commencing in 1867 with a proposed molecular structure for benzene, covered varied fields including the measurement of high temperatures, the chemistry of the electric arc, and the way the eye responds to light. In 1872, during experiments into the specific heats of substances at very low temperatures, he was troubled by the problem of insulating the sample from extraneous sources of heat. His solution was to enclose the experiment inside a vacuum jacket, so that heat transfer by conduction and convection through the surrounding air was eliminated. Twenty years later he used this principle to construct the *Dewar flask,* in which liquid gases could be stored at very low temperatures for long periods.

Dewar flasks are still used for this purpose, and the domestic vacuum flask was quickly developed commercially. It is curious that Dewar took no steps to patent the device, which could have made him a wealthy man.

It was at this point that Dewar took up the low-temperature studies with which his name is generally associated. In 1874 there appeared two important papers: *The Latent Heat of Liquid Gases,* read at the British Association, and *A New Method of Obtaining Very Perfect Vacua.* The subject of the second paper was the absorptive powers of charcoal, which could be used, Dewar discovered, to remove the last gaseous molecules from a high vacuum produced by the usual mechanical pump methods. Later, after he had produced liquid air, he found that charcoal cooled in this medium had its absorptive powers tremendously increased, and the very high vacua obtained through its use were of great importance to physicists working with elementary atomic particles. Charcoal was also used in gas masks issued during the First World War.

The physicist L P Cailletet (1832-1913) achieved the partial liquefaction of oxygen in 1877 by compressing it to a pressure of 300 atmospheres (4400 psi) and obtaining a vapour. Dewar, in 1884, was the first person to collect true liquid oxygen, and he demonstrated the process before an audience at the Royal Institution. The principle employed was to compress the gas, and then to allow it to expand through a valve into an evacuated chamber, at which point a sharp drop in temperature occurred. Solid oxygen was obtained two years later, and in 1895 he succeeded in collecting hydrogen vapour. Liquid hydrogen was obtained in 1898, but he failed in his attempt to liquefy helium because of the presence of neon, which froze relatively easily and blocked the valves of his apparatus. The success of his attempts, where others had failed, was largely due to his vacuum insulating jacket.

During the period 1888-1891 he was a member of a government committee on explosives, and during this time, in conjunction with Sir Frederick Augustus Abel (1827-1902), he invented the propellant explosive cordite. Another committee on which he served concerned itself with the purity of the London water supply, and, like his contemporary Sir William CROOKES, he was consulted on sewage disposal.

Married with no children, a gourmet, and a lover of music and fine arts, Dewar was generally acknowledged as a poor teacher, a good lecturer, and a magnificent experimentalist. A great many honours came his way. He was President of the Chemical Society in 1897, and of the British Association in 1902. Elected a Fellow of the Royal Society in 1877, he was awarded its Rumford Medal in 1894, and was knighted in 1904. He died in London on 27 March 1923.

Below: James Dewar in his laboratory. He is best remembered for his researches on cryogenic (low-temperature) chemistry. In 1898 he was the first to produce liquid hydrogen in quantity, but failed in the case of the lower boiling helium, the lowest boiling element of all.

Below: some early Dewar vacuum flasks; these led to the development of a double-walled vessel with a high vacuum in between the walls for insulation, and made of silvered glass to reflect away heat.

RONAN PICTURE LIBRARY

MICHAEL HOLFORD LIBRARY

DIAMOND

Diamonds were first discovered over two thousand years ago in India and Borneo. In 1725 the Brazilian diamond fields were discovered, followed in 1866 by the South African diamond strike. Today Africa and Russia are the biggest producers of mined diamonds; since 1953 diamonds have also been produced synthetically. Diamonds are not only among the rarest and most beautiful of jewels, but are of incalculable importance to modern industry and technology.

Geological source
The source of diamonds is an *igneous* (of volcanic origin) rock called *kimberlite*. Kimberlite occurs in volcanic pipes and fissures, usually nearly circular in shape, and varying in size from a few metres in diameter to several hundred acres. Kimberlite contains characteristic accessory minerals, such as mica, garnet and zircon, which serve as indicators for geologists searching for kimberlite, but not all kimberlites contain diamonds. In its original state, kimberlite is grey-blue in colour, and is called *blue ground;* it weathers with exposure to air to a yellowish clay called *yellow ground.* Diamonds are mined either from kimberlite pipes or from *alluvial* deposits (deposited by flowing water).

To form these, kimberlite brought to the surface by volcanic action has been eroded by the weather and carried away by river systems to be redeposited, often far from the original source. The most important alluvial deposit in Africa was built up along the Atlantic coast in this manner; it is now mined by Consolidated Diamond Mines of South West Africa. The diamonds were probably carried by the Orange River from a distant inland source.

It is estimated that in 2000 years only about 230 tons of diamonds have been mined; to obtain this yield at least 5000 million tons of rock, sand and gravel have been moved. In alluvial deposits there are usually between 15 and 30 million parts of waste to one part of diamond.

Mining techniques
Originally, kimberlite deposits were all worked by simple opencast methods. The greatest opencast depth was about 240 m (800 feet) at Kimberley, South Africa. A typical example of opencast mining today is the Finsch pipe, which at its widest point is 535 m (1750 feet) in diameter. Up to 12 m (40 feet) of topsoil and rubble were removed to expose the kimberlite, which goes down at least 300 m (1000 feet). Mining is carried out in 12 m (40 feet) levels. The kimberlite is blasted along the rims of these levels and carried in dump trucks to treatment plants.

Underground mining of kimberlite pipes involves working at considerable depths, such as 900 m (3000 feet) in the Kimberley mines.

The oldest underground mining method is *chambering,* developed at Kimberley about 1890. Shafts thousands of feet deep are sunk well away from the pipe. Horizontal shafts are then driven into the pipe, and from them a complex of short tunnels is driven into the blue ground, forming a system of chambers from which the blue ground is removed mechanically. Up to 5000 tons a day may be removed. This method has largely been abandoned in favour of others with higher production potential, such as *block caving.*

In this method shafts known as scraper drifts are taken across the pipe from a haulage shaft outside the pipe. In the sides of these drifts, inclined openings 1.2 m (4 ft) square are left approximately every 3.5 m (11 ft). These are the draw points for the mined ore, and are staggered on opposite sides of the drifts. Above these draw points, cones are excavated

Left: setting a web of fuses in preparation for blasting at De Beers' Premier mine.

Top: chunks of kimberlite, 'blue ground', being conveyed to the crushing machinery, the first step in separating the diamond from the other minerals.

Above: the grease belt method of separating diamond from the rest of the concentrate. The diamonds adhere to the grease.

DIAGRAM

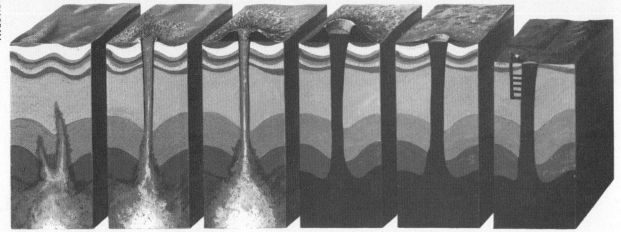

Above: the formation of a kimberlite pipe. As the pressure of the molten magma builds up the rock above it begins to crack. The crack reaches the surface and a lava cone forms. This weathers and is eroded, and can eventually be mined.

Below: cutaway of a diamond mine showing the block caving method. Inclined cone shaped openings are left in the sides of the concrete lined scraper drifts. The kimberlite above these draw points caves in, falls into the tunnel and is taken away to the crushing machine.

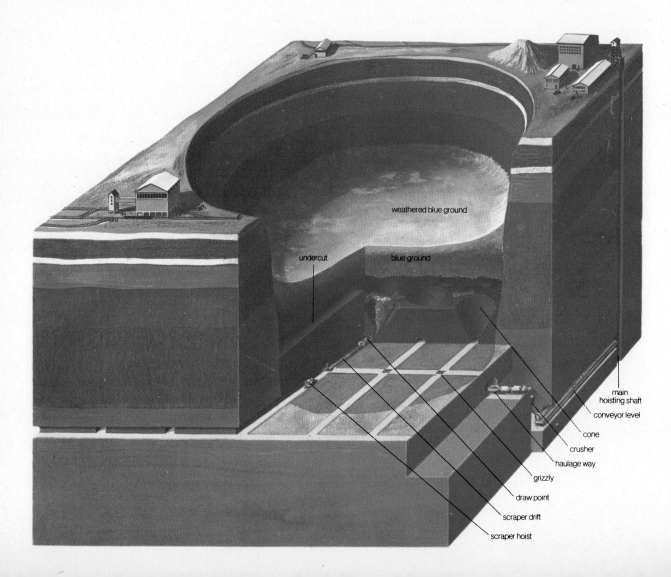

weathered blue ground

undercut

blue ground

main hoisting shaft

conveyor level

cone

crusher

haulage way

grizzly

draw point

scraper drift

scraper hoist

in the pipe. A horizontal slice, 2.2 m (6 ft) high, is then mined out above the cones over the entire area of the pipe. This operation leaves the mass of kimberlite hanging without support; it starts breaking up and falls into the cone shaped openings, gravitating to the draw points in the scraper drift below. Mechanical scrapers are used to load the broken kimberlite into trucks for transportation to underground crushers, from where it is hoisted to the surface. When waste rock appears at the draw points in the scraper drifts, mining of that block is complete, and production commences from the next level, several hundred metres lower down, where in the meantime everything has been prepared for similar block caving operations.

The alluvial mining at the Consolidated Diamond Mines of South West Africa is typical of alluvial mining in general. The first step is removal of overburden, involving the handling of some 2,500,000 m³ (88,300,000 feet³) of sand each month. The overburden is removed by diesel-powered scrapers. The gravel bed thus exposed is bulldozed into stockpiles for delivery to a screening plant. A high percentage of diamonds in terrace gravels occurs at or near the bedrock underneath; the bedrock must therefore be cleaned very thoroughly. Where conditions permit, a giant vacuum cleaner called a Vacuveyer is used. As the mining face advances, the overburden is used to backfill the cleaned bedrock behind it.

To mine diamonds from the bottom of the ocean off the coast of South West Africa, the Marine Diamond Corporation used large floating plants which sucked up the gravel from the sea bed. This operation has now been discontinued.

Recovering diamonds from ore

Because diamonds must be recovered from ore undamaged, and because their presence cannot be determined by chemical assay, specialized methods are needed. The first step is to carefully crush or mill the rock to free the diamonds, after which one of several gravity-concentration devices is used to separate the diamond-rich fraction—the *concentrate*—from the barren portion—the *tailings*.

Gravity concentration devices include the rotary washing pan and several types of heavy media separators. The washing pan, developed in Kimberley around 1874, is filled with *puddle*, made from decomposed kimberlite and water, and viscous enough to keep the lighter particles in suspension. The diamond and heavy minerals sink to the bottom while the lighter fraction floats out of the pan via a tailings overflow.

There are three basic types of heavy media separators: the cone, the lifting wheel and the hydrocyclone. The heavy medium is a slurry, usually of ferro-silicon powder, with a density of 2.7 to 3.1 times that of water. Light particles float on the surface and heavy ones sink and are collected. The cone-type device is a cone-shaped tank with a cone-shaped agitator inside it which clears the sides of the tank enough to allow the heavier particles to sink past it, while keeping the slurry agitated so that the lighter particles flow off at the top. The lifting-wheel device is a wheel with lifting paddles inside it which is half filled with slurry. The paddles pick up the heavy particles as they sink to the bottom and dump them in a sink at the top. The hydrocyclone sets up a vortex swirl out of which the heavy particles are pulled by CENTRIFUGAL FORCE.

The separated gravity concentrate is then passed over a grease table, or grease belt, with plenty of water. The greased surface separation technique was invented in Kimberley in 1896. Diamonds from freshly mined kimberlite will adhere tenaciously to grease because they are not easily *wetted* by water. The other heavy minerals are readily wetted and are therefore washed off the table. Periodically the diamonds are scraped off the table and boiled in water to remove the grease. The recovery rate of the grease table is over 99%.

Other, less efficient methods of separation include the use of electrostatic, magnetic or optical devices.

Synthesis of diamonds

Until 1953 all diamonds were mined. In that year the Swedish firm ASEA achieved the synthesis of diamond by simultaneous application of intense heat and pressure to carbon.

Carbon crystallizes in two main forms: graphite and diamond. In diamond the carbon atoms are held in a very tight, regular pattern; in graphite the pattern is looser and less symmetrical. The density of diamond is 3.52 (compared to granite, 2.5 and graphite, 2.3). To produce such a strongly bonded crystal requires the application of great energy. Early diamond synthesis researchers theorized that if intense heat could be applied to graphite to loosen the bonds between the carbon atoms, and ultra high pressure to force the atoms close together, the increased density might be attained.

During the nineteenth century many unsuccessful attempts were made to do this, but the technical problems were too formidable. Temperatures of 2000°C and pressures of 90,000 atmospheres were required, and no apparatus could be constructed to withstand such treatment.

ASEA solved the problem after 23 years of design and development work by constructing a remarkable hydraulic press consisting of six pyramid shaped pistons. Through one segment electrical heating leads were let in. The pressure generated at the centre of the sphere formed by the pistons was equal to the pressure applied at the outer faces of the pistons multiplied by the ratio of the outer to the inner face areas. Thus an applied pressure of around 5800 atmospheres was boosted to 97,000 atmospheres.

Success came on 15 February 1953. About 40 small crystals were produced, which it was estimated had cost the company £140,000 ($336,000) to make.

Since then diamond synthesis has been accomplished in

Below: a diamond-tipped turning tool produces a satisfactory finish on a diesel engine piston in a single pass. No other material makes such precise, long-wearing cutting tools as diamond.

SUNDAY TELEGRAPH

many countries, including the USA, the USSR, South Africa and Japan. The latest plant to be established is in Eire, where in the factory of the De Beers Industrial Diamond Division on the Shannon Airport Industrial Estate millions of carats are made each year. (There are 142 carats to the ounce.)

Synthetic diamonds have the same physical, chemical and optical properties as natural diamonds. They appear pale gold or grey-black in colour; to date the largest size crystal that can be economically produced is about 1 mm, and these are used only for industrial purposes.

Industrial diamonds Diamonds were supposedly used for engraving in Roman times. In 1819 a patent was issued in England for drawing wire through a diamond die, and a diamond drill was first used in 1864. In 1870 diamond lathe tools were manufactured in New York. In 1900, 700,000 carats of industrial quality diamonds were used, whereas world consumption today is somewhere between sixty and seventy million carats per annum. Diamond's role as the world's most important ABRASIVE came about in the 1920s and 1930s when engineers began looking for something to shape ultra-hard carbide tool bits, which were being increasingly used as cutting surfaces in machine tools.

Next to its hardness, the most important physical characteristic of diamond is its crystallographic planes along which it can be cleaved (see DIAMOND CUTTING). By crushing, or in effect, repeated cleaving, diamond can be graded into different sizes and shapes for different applications. About 75% of all industrial diamond is used as abrasive powder. Mixed with resins, metals or ceramics, it forms the cutting surfaces of grinding wheels, bandsaws, files, drills, hones, saw blades and many other tools used to cut or shape everything from glass and ultra-hard metals to stone and concrete. As a polishing powder it gives superb finishes.

In some applications, for example, drilling oil wells and drilling holes in concrete, diamonds are used whole and uncrushed. Wire can be drawn through a diamond die at speeds of up to 100 miles an hour (160 km/h), which would destroy a metal die in seconds. Diamonds polished to a precise shape are used as styli (needles) in record players; they last much longer than other materials.

The speed, relative quietness and precision of diamond tools as opposed to percussion tools is obviously to be preferred in working concrete. Builders are increasingly specifying diamond tools for grinding out-of-level concrete, for cutting core samples and necessary holes for ducts and conduits in buildings and monuments, and to cut expansion and contraction joints in pavement to prevent random cracking. Diamond bladed concrete planers produce an antiskid water shedding surface, solving the problem of aquaplaning on airport runways and roads.

Automation in industry, requiring tools which work to close tolerances over long periods without attention, utilizes the extra life of diamond tools. Turning phosphor-bronze, a good high-speed steel tool cuts a path five miles long; a diamond tool will last 1250 miles. Tolerances of .0001 inch (.0025 mm) can be maintained with a diamond tool; no other tool can maintain such precision for so long. Diamonds are involved in the manufacture of almost everything today which is made to precise dimensions or made of exotic materials, from nose cones and heat shields for space rockets to ruby laser rods and printed microcircuits.

DIAMOND, SYNTHETIC (see gemstones, synthetic)

DIAMOND CUTTING and POLISHING

Rough natural diamonds can be divided into four principal shape categories: stones, cleavages, maccles and flats. Very few diamonds are flawless. Most contain spots and various other types of inclusion, usually carbon, and these may be invisible to the naked eye. The position of flaws, and their size, is important in the cutting of a clean gemstone.

The principal diamond cutting centres are Antwerp, Bombay, New York, Amsterdam and Tel Aviv, but cutting is also carried out in many other countries. Each centre has grown accustomed to cutting a particular category of diamond; Antwerp specializes mainly in cutting cleavages, maccles and chips, the United States in stones, while Amsterdam, Israel and India cut mostly small brilliants.

Although it is the hardest natural substance, a diamond can be shaped and faceted. This is because it has planes of relative weakness, along which, if expertly handled, it can be cleaved cleanly in two. A diamond crystal has hard and soft faces, and on each face there are hard and soft directions. (Relatively speaking, even the soft direction is incredibly hard.) Therefore, if diamonds are crushed a powder is obtained which can be used to polish other diamonds, since when polishing, many of the particles in the powder present their hard directions to the soft direction of the diamond face being polished.

The four processes used in making a gemstone are *cleaving, bruting, sawing* and *polishing*.

Cleaving Cleaving is used before polishing to obtain an improved shape from an irregularly shaped stone, or to split the rare large stones into manageable pieces. A skilled and experienced worker can determine the cleavage plane direction and then, on an edge which is relatively soft, make a

Above: cleaving a diamond. A mark called a kerf has been scratched on the stone with another diamond. A metal blade is inserted in the kerf and tapped sharply in the direction of the plane of cleavage.

Top right: bruting a diamond. A diamond can be roughly rounded by pressing another diamond against it while it spins in a chuck.

Below right: polishing a diamond. Facets are polished by mounting the stone in a device similar to a record player arm which presents it to the polishing wheel. Diamond polishing powder is used. The operator's skill is essential in presenting the stone correctly.

scratch mark, known as a *kerf,* with the hard edge of another diamond. A metal blade, with its plane parallel to the cleavage plane, is then inserted in the kerf, and tapped sharply with a wooden mallet; if this is done correctly the diamond will cleave in two.

Sawing
Preliminary shaping is often done with a high speed slitting saw, a thin disc of phosphor-bronze run at about 5000 rpm. The edge of the disc is covered with a paste of fine diamond dust and olive oil. It is a particularly useful process when cutting across a cleavage plane.

Bruting
Bruting is a rounding process carried out before polishing. The diamond to be polished is mounted in a lathe chuck and another diamond pressed against it as it revolves, roughly rounding it.

Polishing
Diamond powder is rubbed on or impregnated into a cast iron wheel known as a *scaife.* The diamond to be polished is mounted in a *dop* and *tang.* The dop is the holder into which the diamond is fixed with solder, or held mechanically. The tang, acting rather like a record player arm presents the diamond to the revolving scaife. Because of diamond's hard and soft directions the correct presentation of the diamond to the wheel is one of the essential skills of the diamond polisher.

The most widely used cut is the brilliant-cut, which requires 58 separate faceting operations. A large diamond can take months to polish. Other popular cuts are the Emerald, Oval, Pear and Marquise.

Polishing has been traditionally the craft of the individual. Recently, however, a new machine, The Piermatic, has been developed which automatically polishes diamonds up to half a carat with great efficiency.

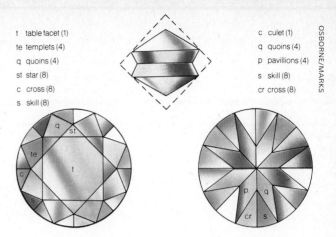

t	table facet (1)	c	culet (1)
te	templets (4)	q	quoins (4)
q	quoins (4)	p	pavillions (4)
st	star (8)	s	skill (8)
c	cross (8)	cr	cross (8)
s	skill (8)		

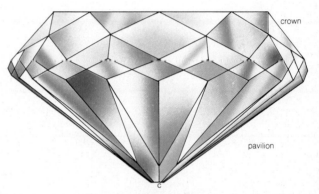

crown

pavilion

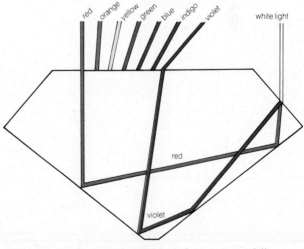

red orange yellow green blue indigo violet   white light

red

violet

Top: how two brilliant-cut diamonds come from a stone, or full crystal. Cleavages, maccles and flats are less regular fragments.

Next from top: three views of a brilliant: the crown or top part has 33 facets and the pavilion or lower part has 24 or 25, depending on whether it has a flat bottom facet or culet.

Above: the brilliant cut gives the most 'fire' and 'life' to a diamond because it is proportioned to reflect all the colours into which an entering ray of white light is split. This diagram shows how light is refracted, split and reflected—the degree of split is exaggerated.

DIECASTING

Diecasting includes several CASTING processes which differ in detail but are all characterized by the use of a permanent metal mould. In the UK the term means both gravity casting and pressure casting; in the USA the former is called permanent mould casting and pressure methods are known as diecasting.

Gravity casting
The simplest diecasting process is the gravity method. The molten metal is poured into the mould and flows by means of gravity. Gravity diecasting is not suitable for complicated castings because of the slowness with which the molten metal fills the cavities of the mould. The gravity process is characterized by relatively high initial costs because of the cost of the mould, but lower production costs. In this respect it is intermediate between sand casting and pressure diecasting.

Pressure diecasting
Pressure diecasting has been developed because of the need to provide large numbers of cheap parts for assembly line production methods. (An automobile will have as many as 250 parts in it which are diecast, from door handles to aluminium alloy engine blocks.) Some simple diecast items can be produced on automatic machinery at the rate of hundreds per minute. Pressure diecasting machinery is expensive and complicated to design, because it has three functions: to inject the molten metal into the die, to clamp the two halves of the die together at forces which may be as high as several thousand tons, and to eject the finished casting when it has solidified. The costs of such machinery can only be recouped over long production runs. Since a die of only moderate complexity could cost over £1000 [$2200], the pressure diecasting process would be considered only for orders of over 5000 pieces.

Pressure diecasting processes are divided into two types: cold chamber and hot chamber methods. In the cold chamber method the molten metal is ladled into a cylinder and then shot into the mould by a hydraulic or pneumatic plunger. In the hot chamber method, the injection cylinder itself is immersed in the molten alloy and successive shots are made either by a plunger or by compressed air. There are also high pressure techniques and low pressure, the latter developed recently in an effort to extend the versatility of diecasting to alloys of higher melting points. Another relatively recent development is the vacuum mould, in which a vacuum is produced in the mould, enabling the pressure shot to fill the mould faster.

Diecasting alloys are in the main alloys of low melting point. Almost the entire production of zinc-based alloys is used in the die casting industry. The higher the melting point the shorter the useful life of the mould: a tool steel die may be able to produce up to half a million castings in zinc, but the total for brass may be only a few thousand. Dies are in use in the pewter industry which are over a hundred years old. Research is continuing into the possibility of casting alloys with higher melting points. If items made of tool steel, for example, could be mass produced by automated casting methods, the savings to industry would be enormous, because the cost of machining such items is great. The technology of diecasting is already such that pieces which have to be precise can be cast close enough to tolerance so that machine finishing is not necessary.

The moulds used in automated diecasting methods are designed with water circulation tubing in them to cool the castings rapidly. The machine opens the mould so that the half of the casting which cools quickest is uncovered first; then ejecting pins push the casting out of the other half of the mould. The two halves of the mould have been coated with grease on the inside beforehand to facilitate the ejection of the finished casting.

DIELECTRIC AND DIELECTRIC CONSTANT (see capacitance)

Above: a selection of items which can be diecast using low pressure methods. Car wheels, casings for pumps and gearboxes, and many other items can be cheaply mass-produced this way.

Right: novelty items diecast from zinc. These are moneyboxes in the shape of ducks which were given away in a promotional scheme. Such an item can be diecast in two halves and fastened together.

DIESEL-ELECTRIC PROPULSION

Railway locomotives and railcars are usually powered by a diesel-electric system, in which the mechanical power of the DIESEL engine is converted to electric power to drive the wheels.

Locomotives with internal combustion engines mechanically coupled directly to the drive wheels have been built, but have not been satisfactory, because they cannot pull the tremendous weight from a standing start, and are not easily adapted to changing load requirements. Using a diesel engine to generate electricity, which can be delivered to the drive wheels in a variable amount as required, has been the practical solution.

The first successful diesel-electric vehicle was a 75 hp (56 kW) railcar on the Mellersta-Sodermanlands Railway in Sweden in 1913. Development was retarded in most countries by World War 1, but by 1925 the 1250 hp (933 kW) Lomonosov locomotive had appeared in the Soviet Union. Powers rose steadily until the outbreak of World War 2, particularly in North America, though the higher powers were achieved by double units, for example the 4000 hp (2980 kW) locomotive of the Romanian State Railway. After the war, diesel traction really began to get underway. During the 1950s large numbers of 350 hp (260 kW) and 400 hp (295 kW) electric shunters were followed by locomotives with up to 3300 hp (2460 kW), the

Below: the British Rail High Speed Train, the prototype for the next generation of inter-city trains. In regular service its operating speed is 125 mph (201 k/h); it holds the world speed record for diesel-electric propulsion of 143 mph (231 k/h).

BRITISH TRANSPORT FILMS

latter being the famous Deltic locomotive, though even this was fitted with two engines.

The power outputs in use today range from about 150 hp (112 kW) to 7000 hp (5220 kW), the smaller outputs being used for shunters and the largest coming from two engines. Often the higher powers are used for pulling low speed heavy freight trains in hilly districts, and not necessarily for high speed running, although the 3300 hp (2450 kW) British Rail locomotive can haul passenger trains at speeds in excess of 100 mph (160 km/hr).

Construction In a typical design, the diesel engine is mechanically coupled to a DC generator (see DYNAMO) which feeds a series-wound DC traction motor (for some small vehicles there may be an ALTERNATOR which feeds an AC traction motor). The motor is normally mounted resiliently on the bogie truck (the undercarriage assembly of wheels and axles) by a nose suspension, which consists basically of compression springs or rubber pads. Sometimes, however, the motors are rigidly mounted on the bogie and a resilient drive is used. A pinion GEAR on the motor transmits power to a gearwheel mounted on the axle next to the roadwheel. The gearwheel is usually about four times as big in diameter as the pinion; a typical gear ratio is 19:92. The road wheel is 25% to 50% bigger than the gearwheel.

Depending on the power output required, there may be up to six traction motors. The speed of the locomotive depends on four factors: the speed of the diesel engine (hence of the generator); the excitation of the generator (controlling the voltage supplied to the traction motors); full-field or weak-field operation of the traction motor; and the gear ratio of the pinion and gearwheel.

The engine is usually started by connecting the generator as a series-wound motor by means of the battery, an additional starting field winding being provided: the engine turns over, fires and runs to idling speed. The starting circuits then revert to normal.

There is also an auxiliary generator, driven by belts or gears from the main generator or mounted on an extension of the main generator shaft. This generator, normally DC, is used to supply the control circuits, the auxiliary circuits and to charge the battery. The output voltage of the auxiliary generator, hence the battery-charging voltage, is maintained substantially constant by a VOLTAGE REGULATOR.

Batteries range from two 12 V batteries on the smallest models, to enable 12 V and 24 V commercial components to be used, to 110 V, which is standard in many parts of the

Opposite page: another application of diesel-electric power. The 'Norma', engaged in the rebuilding of the entrance to Rotterdam harbour, drops 43-ton concrete blocks to form a new breakwater. The 'Norma' and three other vessels are each fitted with four 1000 hp diesels, each driving a compound alternator which provides power for two propellers, fore and aft, giving great manoeuvrability. The project will also provide land for new industry.

Below: a diesel engine in a Hawker-Siddeley 4000 hp 'Co-Co' loco.

PHOTRI

world; some American and Australian vehicles use 74 V.

Controls   Control of the vehicle is by means of a master controller, which is essentially a series of cam-operated switches arranged in groups and interlocked to prevent incorrect operation. The *control group* controls the speed of the vehicle and the *reverse group* controls the direction. The reverse group operates a power switch in the field circuit of each traction motor; it switches the direction of field current, the direction of armature current staying the same. This causes the armature, and hence the vehicle, to reverse.

The function of the control group and circuits is to adjust the excitation of the main generator so that its output voltage applied to the traction motors is also adjusted. This is often accomplished by varying the amount of resistance in series with the generator shunt-field. The variable RESISTOR is part of the load regulator which is under the control of the diesel engine GOVERNOR.

With the engine at maximum speed and the generator at maximum speed and excitation, the vehicle is at maximum speed under *full-field* conditions. If a resistor is now connected in parallel with each traction motor field, some of the field-current is diverted, and this causes an increase in traction motor speed. This is known as *traction motor field diversion,* or *weak-field,* and makes full use of available engine power.

The various circuits are protected by overload relays, circuit breakers or fuses, so that if a fault occurs power is suspended or cut off. Certain faults are indicated by lights in the driver's cab.

DIESEL ENGINE

The diesel engine is named after its inventor, Rudolf Diesel, whose first working prototype ran in 1897 after many years of research work. Until the late 1920s most of the development of diesel engines took place in Germany, and a great deal of experience was gained from the production of engines for submarines during World War 1. The main companies involved at this time were MAN and Daimler-Benz (makers of Mercedes-Benz cars).

The first successful diesel engines for road transport appeared in 1922, although unsuccessful attempts had been made to produce such engines since as early as 1898. Diesel engines of this type during the 1920s were of two, four or six cylinder designs producing about 40 to 50 horsepower.

The use of diesels for marine applications dates from about 1910, but it was not until 1929, with the introduction of designs by Cummins in the USA and Gardner in Britain, that they became a practical proposition for powering small boats. These engines were subsequently adapted for road use.

Power outputs increased steadily during the 1930s, and by the beginning of World War 2 diesel engines were in widespread use in road transport, rail locomotives, tractors and construction plant, ships and boats, and as industrial power sources (including electricity generating sets). For cars, motorcycles and aircraft, however, the diesel could not compete with the petrol [gasoline] engine in terms of performance, although it is still widely used for taxis where economy and durability are more important than high performance.

HAWKER-SIDDELEY

Operating principles The diesel engine, like the petrol engine, is a form of internal combustion engine, and although the two have much in common there are important differences in their respective operating principles. In a petrol engine, fuel and air are mixed in the carburettor, and the mixture is drawn into the combustion chamber at the top of the cylinder during the downward stroke of the piston. The next upward stroke of the piston compresses the mixture to between a sixth and a tenth of its original volume, and as the piston reaches its upper limit of travel the mixture is ignited by an electric spark created by the spark plug. The resulting expansion of the burning mixture forces the piston back down the cylinder (the power stroke).

In a diesel engine, however, as the piston moves down, only pure air is drawn into the cylinder and compressed as it moves up again, but it is compressed to a much higher degree than in a petrol engine (with compression ratios of between 12:1 and 25:1) with the result that its temperature is raised considerably, to well over 1000°F (538°C). As the piston nears the top of its travel a fine spray of fuel is injected into the cylinder by an injector nozzle near the top. The fuel mixes with the air, which has become so hot due to compression that the fuel/air mixture ignites spontaneously without the need for a spark.

As the volume of air drawn into the cylinder is always the same in a diesel engine, its speed is controlled by the amount of fuel that is injected.

A diesel engine can be adapted to run on almost any fuel from vegetable oils to natural gas and high octane petrol, but the most suitable and widely used diesel fuel is distilled from crude oil and closely related to kerosene. It is much less volatile than petrol, with a flash point (temperature at which a heated petroleum product gives off enough vapour to flash momentarily when a small flame is placed nearby) of around 168°F (75°C) whereas the flash point of petrol is lower than ordinary atmospheric temperatures.

Fuel injection The fuel is delivered to each injector by a fuel pump, and there is either one pump for each injector or else one main pump supplying all the injectors in turn by means of a distributor valve. Where there is a pump for each injector the pumps may be grouped together in a single unit, supplying the injectors through feed pipes, or else the pumps and injectors may be combined into individual units with a separate unit mounted on each cylinder. The pumps are of the reciprocating type, with spring loaded plungers actuated by a camshaft driven by the engine. The accelerator control is connected to the pump mechanism, and alters the engine speed by varying the amount of fuel delivered to the injectors.

The injectors have spring loaded needle valves that are opened by the pressure of the shots of fuel delivered by the pumps at the correct instant in the firing cycle. The fuel is sprayed out through holes in the end of the injector, which break it up into a fine mist and distribute it correctly around the combustion chamber (see FUEL INJECTION).

Combustion chambers The fuel-air mixture should burn evenly and progressively, as a violent detonation of the mixture causes an uneven running condition known as 'diesel knock'. To achieve correct combustion the fuel and air must be thoroughly mixed. On engines which have the fuel injected directly into the combustion chamber, more effective

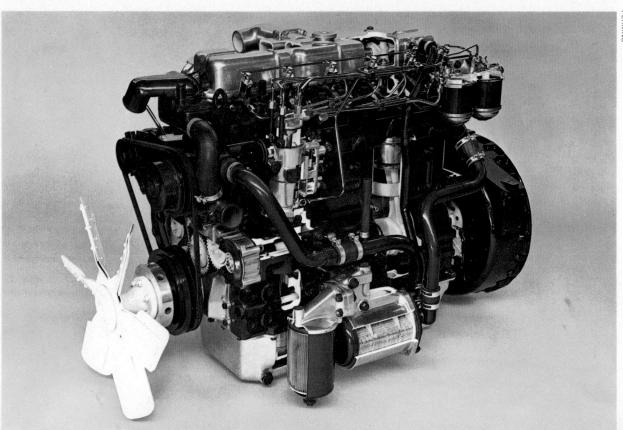

PERKINS

mixing may be achieved by creating turbulence in the air in the cylinder as it is compressed. This is often done by contouring the crown of the piston so that the air is moved around within the cylinder during compression.

Other designs of engine use *swirl chambers* or *pre-combustion chambers* to improve combustion. A swirl chamber is a small spherical chamber above or at the side of the main combustion chamber, and connected to it by a passage. When the air in the cylinder is compressed some of it is forced into the swirl chamber, where a turbulent effect is created due to the shape of the chamber. The fuel is injected into the swirl chamber, and preliminary combustion occurs forcing the mixture into the main combustion chamber where complete combustion takes place.

The pre-combustion chamber is connected to the main combustion chamber by a number of fine passages, and the fuel is injected into it. Part of the mixture in the chamber ignites and expands, forcing the remaining unburnt fuel through the connecting passages, from which it emerges into the main chamber as a fine spray and ignites smoothly.

Two stroke diesels Many diesel engines work on the two stroke principle, and as they only need to draw in pure air instead of the usual air fuel oil mixture needed by the two stroke petrol engine they are more efficient. The intake of fresh air and the expulsion of the exhaust gases is known as 'scavenging', and the two commonest methods used on diesels are *loop scavenging* and *uniflow scavenging*, both of which employ a blower unit to blow the air into the inlet ports.

In the loop scavenging system, as the piston nears the bottom of its stroke it uncovers the inlet and exhaust ports; the inlet port directs air from the blower into the cylinder in an upward direction, and this forces the exhaust gases downwards and out of the exhaust port on the opposite side of the cylinder. As the piston moves back upwards it covers the ports which effectively seals the cylinder, and the clean air is compressed before the fuel is injected into the top of the cylinder.

The uniflow system also has an inlet port in the side of the cylinder, near the bottom, but the exhaust gases are expelled through one or more valves in the top of the combustion chamber. The valves open just before the inlet port is uncovered, and at this point the gases are still under some pressure which starts them flowing out of the cylinder, the remaining gases being expelled by the upward flow of clean air from the blower.

Some two stroke diesels work on the opposed-piston principle, with two pistons in the same cylinder acting in opposition to each other, moving towards the centre of the cylinder from opposite ends. The pistons may be connected by a crank arrangement to the same crankshaft, or may have separate crankshafts coupled by a gear train. The inlet and exhaust ports are near the opposite ends of the cylinder, and the fuel injector is at the centre. At the point of ignition the two pistons are very close together, crown to crown, and the force of the combustion forces them in opposite directions down the cylinder. One piston uncovers the exhaust ports slightly before the other uncovers the inlet ports, and most of the exhaust gas rushes out under pressure, the remainder being expelled by the incoming air when the inlet port is uncovered.

PERKINS

Left: a modern six cylinder turbocharged diesel engine, the 5.8 litre (354 cu in) Perkins T6.354. The latest road version of this engine produces 143 brake horsepower at a speed of 2,600 revs/min, and weighs 1,060 lbs (482 kg). In comparison an unturbocharged version develops only 118 brake horsepower at a speed of 2,800 revs/min, and weighs 925 lbs (420 kg). The turbocharged industrial and marine models of this engine produce 160 brake horsepower at 2,500 revs/min. Higher power outputs are obtainable from the marine versions of diesel engines than can be obtained from the automotive units because better cooling is possible. Marine diesels are usually cooled by a closed circuit fresh water system, the fresh water being cooled in a heat exchanger fed with a supply of cold sea water.

Right: an engine under test in a Perkins sound absorbing chamber designed specifically for research into diesel engine noise sources.

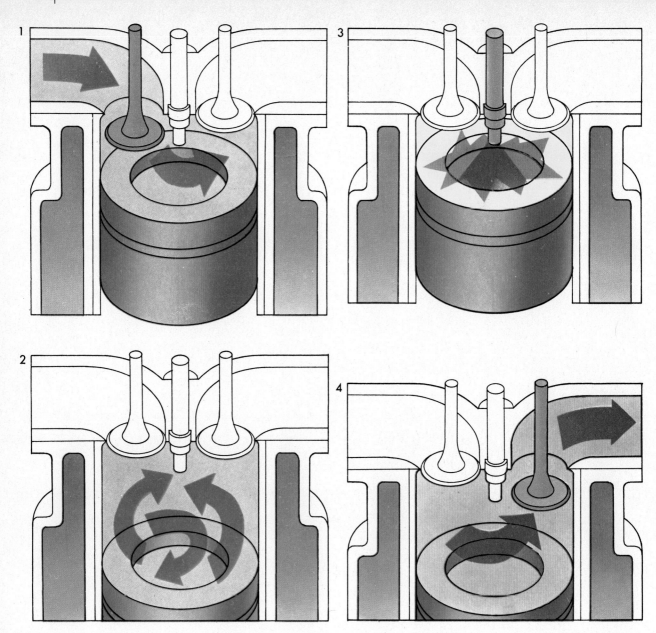

Stages in the combustion cycle of a four stroke diesel engine.

1. *Induction. Air is drawn into the cylinder through the inlet valve.*
2. *Compression: the piston rises compressing the air in the cylinder to very much higher ratios than the ordinary petrol engine.*
3. *Ignition: fuel oil is injected into the compressed air now at a very high temperature and ignites explosively (spontaneously) oil—fine droplets—expands as the piston falls.*
4. *Exhaust: gases formed during the ignition are expelled on the upward stroke of the piston.*

1 oil filter	9 camshaft	16 compressor
2 dipstick	10 cam follower	17 air inlet duct
3 oil scavenge pipe	11 piston	18 water galleries
4 oil pump	12 oil scraper and compression rings	19 cylinder bore
5 crankshaft		20 inlet valve
6 connecting rod	13 turbocharger exhaust duct	21 injector
7 crankshaft journal	14 turbocharger spindle	22 rocker shaft
8 oil pump drive	15 turbocharger turbine	23 rocker

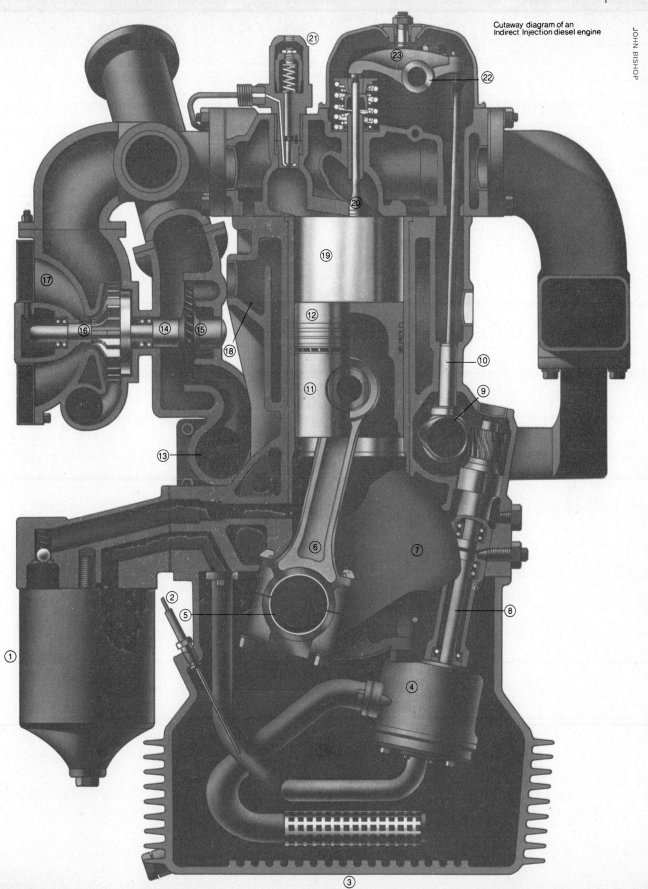

Cutaway diagram of an
Indirect Injection diesel engine

JOHN BISHOP

Supercharging The power output of internal engines can be increased significantly by *supercharging,* and the diesel is well suited to this as only air has to be blown in as opposed to a petrol-air mixture needed by a petrol engine. The SUPERCHARGER drives more air into the cylinders than can be drawn in by the downward motion of the pistons alone, so that more fuel-air mixture can be burnt in a given cylinder volume than on an unsupercharged engine, and thus more power obtained without increasing the size of the engine. The supercharger is a form of COMPRESSOR, driven by the engine, and several types are used including reciprocating, screw, and centrifugal versions, on both two and four stroke diesels. *Turbochargers* are superchargers driven by a small TURBINE which is powered by the exhaust gases.

Starting Diesel engines which have the fuel injected directly into the combustion chamber do not present any special difficulties when starting from cold, other than the need for very powerful starter motors on the larger versions. Engines fitted with pre-combustion or swirl chambers, however, can be difficult to start and usually employ some form of heater plugs or coils, electrically powered and usually mounted next to the injectors, which pre-heat the air in the combustion chambers and help the fuel to vaporize until the engine has warmed up.

Hand starting is quite easy with smaller engines, and can be used on larger industrial models by means of some form of energy storage. This can be done by spinning a large flywheel and coupling it to the engine when it is spinning fast enough, or by building up pressure in a hydraulic cylinder by means of a hand pump, then releasing the energy to a toothed rack which engages a pinion on the engine crankshaft. In some cases a small, easily started engine may be used as a starter motor for a large engine.

Applications The diesel engine is a highly adaptable power source, and a very large range is manufactured all over the world. They can be air cooled or water cooled, two or four stroke, supercharged or unsupercharged, and can be adapted to run on a wide variety of fuels. On land, they are almost universally used in construction plant and commercial vehicles, and are widely used in taxis and increasingly in cars that cover very large annual mileages. Many rail locomotives are diesel or DIESEL-ELECTRIC powered, and most agricultural machines such as tractors and harvesters are powered by diesels.

Stationary units provide sources of power for industry, including drives for compressors and generators. Marine diesels are used to power launches, yachts, fishing boats, some high speed naval boats, tugboats, speedboats and many other small craft.

In the future, the diesel engine may face increased competition from small lightweight gas turbines, and development work is also being carried out on rotary Wankel type diesel engines, which if successful will combine the smooth running and compactness of the turbine with the flexibility of the conventional diesel.

An early diesel powered rail locomotive which was used on the Golden City and San Juan Railway in the United States. This one is now at the Railway Museum in Golden City, which is near Denver, Colorado. Diesel locomotives have been in use since before World War I.

DIESEL, Rudolf (1858-1913)

Rudolf Christian Karl Diesel was an engineer who perfected the type of internal combustion engine that is named after him. He was born in Paris, the son of a German leather worker from Augsburg. Diesel's parents were strict, and the family was very poor. A harsh, insecure upbringing gave Diesel the drive to accomplish great things, but also had its effect on his mental stability.

Diesel was a brilliant student. As a boy he spent many hours in the Paris Museum of Arts and Crafts, where he made drawings of machines, including Cugnot's steam wagon of 1769. At the outbreak of the Franco-Prussian war of 1870, the Diesel family moved to London, where Diesel was fascinated by the machines in the Science Museum. Then he was sent to Augsburg to live with an uncle who was professor of mathematics at the Augsburg trade school. While in Augsburg he saw a pump which created heat by the compression of air, and his later success began to take form.

In 1875 he began attending lectures at the Munich Technical University. Among the lecturers was Carl von Linde, whose research in THERMODYNAMICS had led to the invention of refrigeration techniques. After graduating from the university with the most brilliant record in its history, Diesel went to work for von Linde in his refrigeration company, soon rising to the post of factory manager.

At university Diesel had found that existing engines were not very efficient, and had studied the theories of CARNOT on the efficient transmission of energy in the form of heat. He resolved to build a more efficient engine. In his capacity as von Linde's plant manager, he became interested in the possibility of replacing steam with ammonia vapour, but gave that up in favour of the idea of using the heat from compressed air to ignite a fuel mixture in the cylinder. He patented designs in 1892 and 1893. At first he wanted to use coal dust in his engine, as the cheapest fuel available, but his design required a fluid which could be sprayed into the combustion chamber, so he settled on petroleum oil. His first successful engine was a 25 horsepower single cylinder four stroke model built in 1897. It was displayed at a Munich exhibition in 1898, and the inventor soon became a millionaire.

A diesel engine needs no spark plugs because the fuel is ignited by the heat of the atmosphere in the combustion chamber, which is compressed by the upstroke of the piston. It will run on cheaper fuel than other internal combustion engines. In 1902 it was first used to generate electricity, and in 1903 the first diesel-powered ship was afloat.

Diesel's engine was not the first compression-ignition engine, and some of his patents were contested. A factory he built in Augsburg failed. Some of his early engines broke down; because of the tremendous pressures required, the earliest designs were not reliable. Diesel was a suspicious, difficult man who insisted that the engines be built to his original specifications, delaying improvements which could have been made. In spite of all this, his ability as an engineer was widely recognized, and there was some talk of a Nobel prize.

In 1913 he disappeared during a trip from Antwerp to Harwich on the mail steamer *Dresden* to discuss the sale of his engines to the British Admiralty. There was some speculation that he had been kidnapped or murdered by government agents in the tense atmosphere of pre-World War I Europe, but in fact he had made special preparations at home before leaving, and had spoken of suicide by jumping off a ship.

Above: an 1898 portrait of Rudolf Diesel by Alexander Fuks.

Below: Diesel's first successful engine, which was built in the Maschinenfabrik works at Augsburg in Germany.

DIFFERENTIAL

The differential is a GEAR assembly in a motor vehicle which allows the propeller shaft, or drive shaft, to turn the drive wheels at different speeds when the vehicle is going around a curve. When a vehicle goes around a curve, the wheel on the inside of the curve travels less distance than the other, and so must turn more slowly, for safety in handling and to keep tyre wear to a minimum. A four wheel drive vehicle, such as a Jeep or a Land Rover, has two differentials. For maximum traction, a four wheel drive vehicle has been designed with three differentials, separating the front wheels, the rear wheels and the front from the rear, allowing each wheel to turn at its own speed under power. (The only car which does not have a differential is the Daf car, built in Holland, which has a belt drive system allowing slippage of the belt on the pulleys.)

The differential is encased in a casting, which is located on most cars (having rear wheel drive) in the middle of the rear axles between the wheels. (It is sometimes called the 'cabbage head' because of its bulbous appearance.) The drive shaft enters the casting in the front and one axle enters at each side. A pinion gear, which is splined into the end of the drive shaft, turns a bevelled *crown* gear which is fastened onto the end of one of the axles. An assembly of four small bevelled gears (two pinions and two star gears) is bolted to the crown gear and turns with it. The other axle is driven by the small pinion gear opposite the crown gear. The assembly drives both axles at the same speed when the vehicle is being driven in a straight line, but allows the axle opposite the crown gear to turn slower or faster, as required.

Some units are designed to give a *limited-slip* or *slip-lock* differential, to equalize power between the wheels on a slippery or a soft road surface, providing safe handling and minimizing the likelihood of getting stuck in snow or soft earth.

The *gear ratio* (ratio of the number of teeth on one gear to the number of teeth on the other) between the crown gear and the pinion gear is one of the factors that determines the performance characteristics of the car, such as acceleration and top speed.

Early cars had pinion and crown gears with straight teeth on them, which resulted in noisy operation of the differential and allowed play in the gear teeth, causing undue wear. Today the pinion and crown gears are *helical* gears, which means that the toothed surfaces are bevelled and the teeth themselves are curved. This design eliminates play between the teeth, because as the gears spin together one tooth is in full contact before the previous tooth leaves. A properly constructed differential should last the life of the car without any maintenance at all.

In order to produce a particularly quiet differential, the pinion and crown gears are lapped together in a lapping machine which duplicates the operating conditions of the completed differential. After lapping, the two gears are kept together as a set. They are inspected together in a machine in a quiet room which determines the exact thickness of shims (sheet metal discs used to ensure a close fit) required in the assembly to ensure quiet operation; then they go to the differential assembly line. All the gears in the system are installed against roller bearings, the proper shimming is installed; then the unit is test-run, filled with a heavy oil and sealed. Quiet operation of the differential is essential in a vehicle with unit-body construction, as opposed to a separate body bolted to a frame, because noise from the differential will be transmitted by the body itself.

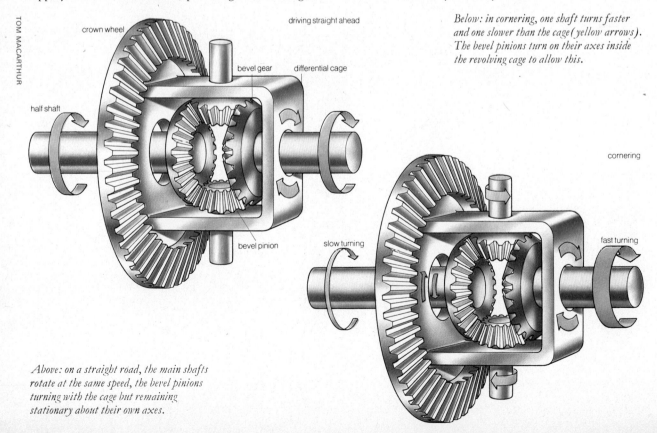

TOM MACARTHUR

crown wheel

driving straight ahead

bevel gear   differential cage

half shaft

bevel pinion

Below: in cornering, one shaft turns faster and one slower than the cage (yellow arrows). The bevel pinions turn on their axes inside the revolving cage to allow this.

cornering

slow turning   fast turning

Above: on a straight road, the main shafts rotate at the same speed, the bevel pinions turning with the cage but remaining stationary about their own axes.

Above: a fork lift truck axle, a completely enclosed assembly. The wheel hubs are on each end and the differential is in the middle. The housings are separate castings to allow for several different axles and wheel offsets, to be matched to different motors or gearboxes. The pinion coupling, seen protruding from the front of the differential casing, can be connected to a gearbox, torque converter or conventional power shaft transmission. The wheel hub casings contain an additional gear reduction assembly.

Below: a cutaway view of a heavy duty truck axle. The large gear at the right is the crown gear of the differential; the wheel of the truck is mounted on the flange facing the front. Power is transmitted from the engine through the transmission shaft, which protrudes from the unit above the crown gear and has half a universal joint fitted to it, to the unit at the rear which in turn drives the pinion in the differential. The unit in the green casing is a two-speed electrically operated gearbox which doubles the gear ratios available.

DIFFRACTION

A seventeenth century Italian Jesuit, Francesco Grimaldi, was the first to discover that light does not travel in exact straight lines, but can bend round obstacles very slightly; this is caused by the phenomenon of diffraction. The effect is put to practical use to analyze light and crystal structure.

Grimaldi found that the shadows of thin rods illuminated by narrow shafts of light were not sharp, as would be expected. Instead, there were bright lines just inside the edge of the shadow. The effect is not normally noticeable unless very small, bright sources of light or fine meshes are used.

If the filament of a clear light bulb or a candle is seen through a fine mesh, for example, the image will be seen to be broken up, with a series of images getting fainter with their distance from the main image. These images may be coloured, being red at one edge and blue the other. This breaking up of the image gives diffraction its name—it comes from the same Latin root as 'fracture'. The same effect is seen when a light is reflected off a fine-grooved record—delicate colours can be seen. Television cameramen use a grid over their camera lenses to produce a starlike effect on bright lights in variety programmes, and the spikes seen on photographs of stars are caused by support vanes inside the telescope used.

Diffraction can be observed in all types of WAVE MOTION: sound and water waves, as well as light, X-rays and radio waves, show the effects. It is because of diffraction, for example, that sound can be heard round corners. Practical observation of sounds heard in this way reveals another feature of diffraction: that long wavelengths are diffracted more than short ones. In the case of a marching band, it is noticeable that the notes which are heard first are those of the bass drum, while the piccolos are not clear until they are directly in view—even though the piccolos may then sound louder. Deep notes have a long wavelength whereas high notes have a short wavelength.

The same effect occurs with light, and gives rise to the coloured fringes associated with diffraction. As with sound, the low frequencies—that is, red light—are bent most, and the high frequencies (blue) are bent least. To produce the effect in a usable form, not just one 'corner' but a large number is required. A diffraction grating consists of a regular series of fine lines ruled on glass, which will either transmit light or, if given a suitable coating, reflect it. The spacing of the lines varies, but in a high quality grating may be as many as 30,000 per inch (12,000 lines/cm).

Dispersion A narrow beam of light falling on such a grating will have bands of colour on either side of the direct image. There are several 'orders' or separate bands: as they get further from the direct image, they become more spread out (*dispersed*) and fainter.

The angle through which a particular colour is diffracted depends on its wavelength and the spacing of the grating's lines. The finer the grating, the more each wavelength will be diffracted and hence the greater the dispersion. A grating intended to diffract microwaves (with wavelengths several million times longer than light) would therefore have a spacing of centimetres rather than thousandths of a centimetre.

X-rays, on the other hand, need much smaller spacings—

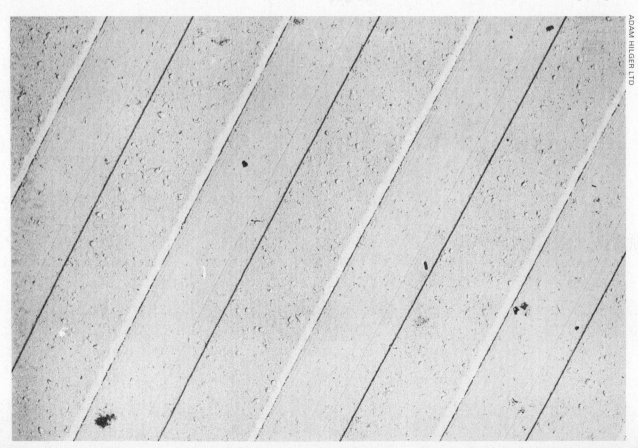

ADAM HILGER LTD

Right: a diffraction grating splits up white light passing through a slit. This grating is aluminized to make it reflect; some of the light which comes through the slit is reflected as from a normal mirror, and some is diffracted into colours. The grating has some 30,000 grooves per inch (1200 per mm) and is 'blazed'—that is, the grooves are cut at an angle in such a way that the diffracted light is thrown only to one side of the white light, rather than to both sides. First and second order diffraction can be seen, the second order being fainter and paler.

Bottom left: diffraction grating grooves enlarged some 5000 times. The grating has 2500 per inch (100 per mm), a size which may be used for infra-red work. The lines are still sharp even at such a high magnification. From 'Dividing, Ruling and Mask-making' by D F Horne. (Adam Hilger, London, 1974).

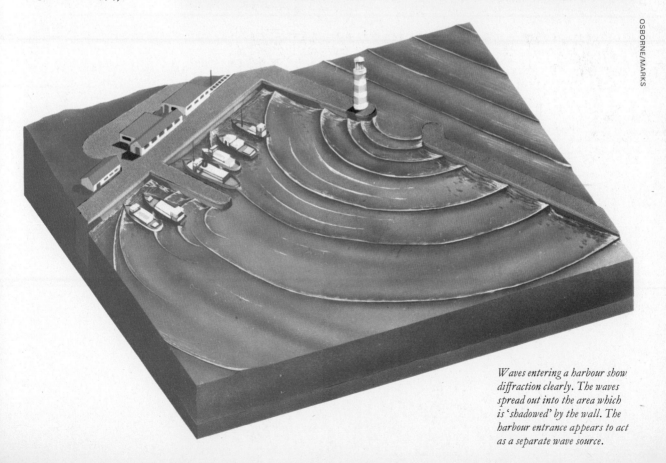

Waves entering a harbour show diffraction clearly. The waves spread out into the area which is 'shadowed' by the wall. The harbour entrance appears to act as a separate wave source.

they have wavelengths thousands of times shorter than light. The regular spacings of the atoms in CRYSTALS will diffract X-rays.

Uses The study of crystal lattices using the X-ray diffraction patterns is known as CRYSTALLOGRAPHY, and techniques of this sort have proved invaluable in studying the properties of crystal structure. Electron and neutron diffraction are also used for this purpose, using the wave properties of matter (see QUANTUM THEORY).

Diffraction gratings are widely used in SPECTROSCOPY, the analysis of light. Gratings produce a completely regular spacing of the wavelengths, whereas prisms, which split light into colours by refraction, spread the short wavelengths out more than the red end. Since the light does not have to pass through the glass, gratings can be used to study wavelengths which would otherwise be absorbed, such as infra-red and ultra-violet.

Although diffraction gratings of high quality have to be carefully ruled on optically flat glass, and are consequently very expensive, replica gratings of plastic materials are much cheaper. The replica is impressed with the fine lines by a high quality master die, in much the same way that a microgroove record is made. Indeed, cheap replicas are used to make eye-catching iridescent brooches.

Physics Diffraction can be explained by using the model of wave behaviour first proposed by the seventeenth century Dutch physicist Christiaan HUYGENS. He suggested that every point on an advancing wavefront can be thought of as a secondary source of waves in its own right. If undisturbed, these secondary waves will combine to form the new wavefront, so advancing it.

When an obstruction is placed in the way, however, some of the secondary waves spread out from the edge of the obstacle, so apparently bending round it. If a series of obstacles is used, these secondary waves may mutually interfere, either reinforcing or destroying each other's effect, so producing light and dark bands of light which are split into colours depending on the dispersion of each wavelength.

The spikes on the stars in this photograph of the Pleiades cluster (the Seven Sisters) are caused by diffraction around support vanes in the telescope used; the rings, however, are a photographic effect.

DIGITAL READOUT DEVICES

The purpose of a digital readout device is to display the measurement of a quantity or the result of a calculation directly in numeric symbols instead of by an indicator moving over a calibrated scale, such as a moving coil voltmeter. This can be done by electromechanical, electrical or electronic devices. The departure and arrival indicators at rail, air and bus terminals are another form of readout display, and are usually electromechanical.

The information to be displayed is usually in the form of an electrical signal, produced by the measuring instrument or other equipment using the readout device, and this signal must be decoded and converted into a suitable form for driving the display. This is known as *interfacing*.

The three main factors that determine which type of display is best suited for a particular application are: the method of interfacing; the requirements of the display itself in terms of its driving mechanism or circuitry and its mounting within the equipment; and the purpose for which the display is required — varying from a 0.1 inch (2.5 mm) high character on a pocket calculator to a 6 inch (15.2 cm) high character on a railway or airport information board.

The types of display available can be broadly divided into three main groups. The first is the electromechanical type, in which the displaying of information involves moving parts, and the second is the electrical type which may be an assembly of filament lamps, or a gas discharge device. The third is the more advanced electronic type using such devices as solid

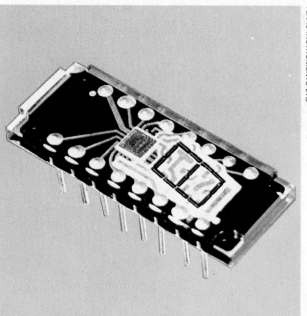

Above: a numeric display module using light emitting diodes (leds), which can be seen in the picture displaying a figure '8'. Light emitting diodes are made from gallium arsenide (GaAs), treated with phosphorus to bring their electromagnetic radiation output into the visible spectrum. The square block situated at the centre of the module, above the led array, is an integrated circuit containing the logic circuitry that drives the display.

Right: an electromechanical indicator board, Euston Station, London.

HALE OBSERVATORIES

TEXAS INSTRUMENTS LTD

light emitters or LIQUID CRYSTALS.

Mechanical displays

The main advantage of mechanical devices is their great flexibility in terms of character style and size. This is important where ease of reading from distances is required. A disadvantage of these devices, however, is the difficulty of driving such a display. This usually involves turning a 'bank' of numbers or letters printed on drums, discs or plates until the required character is on view. This is done with electromagnets, relays and electric motors, and the interfacing of these systems can lead to reliability and servicing problems. These systems are also bulky and expensive to construct. The inherent speed restrictions limit the usefulness of mechanical devices when used in conjunction with logic systems or business machines such as copiers and collating systems. The main uses include relatively slow speed devices such as digital clocks or devices where the information is effectively static for a period of time, for example, the arrival and departure boards used in air, rail and bus terminals.

Electrical displays

The first device used in electrical displays was the filament lamp. On such a display lamps are arranged in a grid or matrix formation, and the characters are produced by illuminating the appropriate pattern of lamps within the matrix. Filament lamp displays and their associated drive circuitry are bulky and expensive, and reliability can be a problem with filaments being prone to failure, especially in situations where they are subjected to severe vibration. Heat dissipation was another problem

which lead to the development of neon devices which are cooler in operation, but these have the disadvantage of higher working voltages. Some applications of filament devices still exist, a prime example being highway information displays and ELECTRONIC NEWSCASTERS.

VALVE [vacuum tube] technology has produced the widely used *nixie tube* displays. These operate on the principle of localized ionization (and thus glowing) of gas around an electrode shaped in the form of the character required. The electrodes are enclosed in a gas filled tube rather like a radio valve, and as an electrode can be included for each of the characters to be displayed (usually the numerals 0 to 9) the LOGIC CIRCUITS needed to drive such a device are minimal. A voltage is applied to the appropriate electrode for whichever number is required, and hence decoding is eliminated. The two main disadvantages are that the numerals are mounted one behind the other within the tube, so that only one number can be displayed at a time in each tube and the characters can have an uneven appearance, and secondly high voltages are normally required (typically 170 volts). This sometimes makes it necessary to include power supplies in the equipment specifically to drive the display, which limits its uses in portable and battery driven equipment.

To combat these disadvantages incandescent filament tubes have been developed, using a seven segment filament that displays the characters on the same plane, which makes them much clearer. This system, however, needs a decoded drive. During operation, the coiled filament segments glow in a

BRITISH RAIL

clear, bright fine line. If a broader line is desired an etched glass screen can be placed in front of the device, and by the use of filters any colour of display can be produced.

A recent form of display is the 'self-scan' gas discharge panel, which has the advantage that high density multi-digit readouts can be included in one panel. Displays are available with from 8 to 400 characters. The digits are arranged in columns of 5×7 dot matrices, and the device scans from left to right one full column at a time. After the last character is displayed a reset pulse in the drive logic is generated to initiate a new scan. The logic circuits and high voltages required can be a disadvantage with this type of display.

Solid state displays

Light emitting SEMICONDUCTOR devices have provided a significant breakthrough in display techniques. These devices utilize the light produced at junctions formed in gallium (a metallic element) compound semiconductors when a current is passed through them. At the present time red, orange, yellow and green units are available, with blue units under development. These light emitting DIODES (leds) are arranged in groups and the characters are produced by activating the appropriate pattern. Electrically the devices may be thought of as simple forward-biased diodes with low voltage and current requirements which are fully compatible with standard INTEGRATED CIRCUITS. The decode and drive logic may be mounted within the same package as the display, which saves space within the equipment and reduces the complexity of the circuit boards.

By using standard integrated circuit techniques, displays may be condensed onto one chip of semiconductor material, giving a monolithic unit of small size for applications such as pocket size calculators. Due to their reliability and low power requirements, light emitting diode displays are becoming widely accepted for many standard readout applications, and are rapidly replacing many of the older types of display.

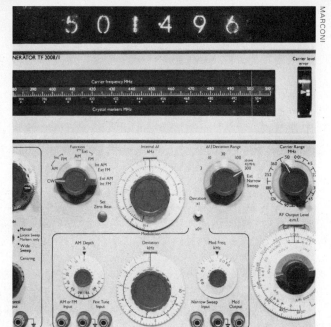

Above: a nixie tube display panel on a 10 kHz to 510 MHz AM/FM signal generator, a test instrument used in radio engineering. The rather uneven appearance of the characters in the display is due to the fact that in the nixie tube type of display device there is a separate electrode for each character, and these are mounted one behind the other. As a result the outlines of the unlit electrodes are often visible in front of the character which is being displayed.

Below: 5 × 7 dot matrix numerical displays.

DIGITIZER

A digitizer is a device which converts *analog,* or continuously varying, quantities into *digital* signals—that is, a series of electrical pulses in the form of a code.

Many measurements in science and industry, such as temperature, pressure, or the speed of a rotating engine shaft for example, are in analog form. So that the measurements can be dealt with by digital COMPUTERS, perhaps in order to control the process which the measurements refer to, they have to be converted into a digital form. Sometimes the reverse function has to be performed, so that a digital signal from a computer can be shown on a GRAPHIC DISPLAY or to control an industrial process.

Analog to digital conversion

To convert analog data into a digital form frequent 'readings' must be taken at intervals—that is, the signal must be *sampled.* Secondly, the overall range of input signal values is divided into a number of steps, or levels, called *quantization levels.* Each of these levels covers a small range of values such that if the signal amplitude of a sample is within that range it is said to occupy that level. A signal can therefore only occupy one level at any one time (sample).

This process gives only an approximation, since if important changes in the signal take place much faster than the sampling rate then information will be lost. A television picture, for example, requires a rate of millions of samples per second. If there are too few quantization levels for the signal, then again information is lost—a TV picture would appear only black or white, with no shades of grey, in a system with only two quantization levels.

Digital coding of speech

To convert speech into a digital form for transmission, a microphone and digitizer are used. The microphone converts the speech pressure waves into an equivalent varying voltage and the electronic digitizer converts this into a digital code.

One form of electronic digitizer compares the incoming analog signal with a linearly increasing voltage—called a ramp voltage. This ramp voltage is synchronized to a counting device, which produces a series of numbers in code, and counts the pulses produced by a pulse generator within the device. When the ramp voltage equals the incoming analog voltage the counter is stopped. The counter number represents the ramp voltage, and therefore the analog signal value, at that moment. This gives one sample value of the signal, which is read from the counter in digital form—either a binary or decimal number. Repeating this process gives a series of sampled values.

In a high fidelity (hi-fi) system where the maximum frequencies to be reproduced approach the limit of hearing (about 18 kHz) the sampling rate must be at least twice this (36 kHz or 36,000 samples per second). Also, for faithful sound reproduction, up to 1024 quantization levels might be used. Using PULSE CODE MODULATION (PCM) where the analog signal amplitude at each sample is represented by a binary number 10 binary digits (bits) are therefore required—the binary code for 1024 consists of 10 bits, each either 0 or 1. In a telephone system such fidelity is not required, sampling rates of 8 kHz and up to 256 quantization levels (8 bits) being typical. These

Below left: in a rotary digitizer a binary coded disc is used to measure shaft movement. A beam of light is focused on the disc, behind which is an array of photocells. Each position of the disc throws a unique light pattern on the cells which produces a corresponding output. This is then converted into a suitable digital form.

Below: in an analog-to-digital converter the analog signal is first quantized, producing a step-like approximation. This is then sampled, producing discrete pulses which can be turned into a binary form.

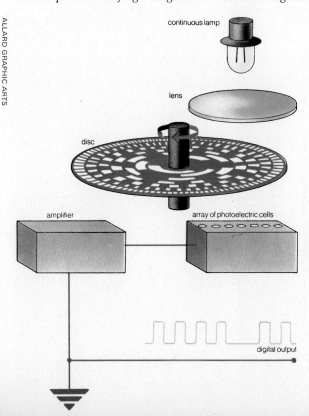

continuous lamp

lens

disc

amplifier

array of photoelectric cells

digital output

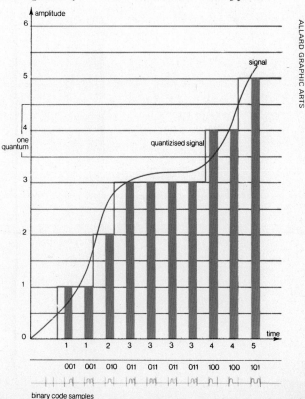

amplitude

signal

one quantum

quantisized signal

time

| 1 | 1 | 2 | 3 | 3 | 3 | 3 | 4 | 4 | 5 |

| 001 | 001 | 010 | 011 | 011 | 011 | 011 | 100 | 100 | 101 |

binary code samples

digital systems are coming into use for a wide variety of communications purposes.

Another system for converting speech into a digital code is delta modulation. The output pulses from this type of digitizer give an on-going 'picture' of the rate of change of the analog signal.

These types of digitizers can be adapted to other applications apart from speech and picture coding. Wherever a physical quantity can be turned into a voltage such a digitizer can be included to turn this into a digital signal. A digital VOLT-METER, for example, is no more than an extremely accurate digitizer with a numerical display (see DIGITAL READOUT DEVICES).

Apart from purely electronic digitizers there are those which use ELECTROMAGNETIC sensing devices, such as in the *area digitizer*, and combined optical and electronic sensing devices, such as in *linear* and *rotary* digitizers.

Area digitizers

This type comprises a drawing board or mat into which a series of parallel wires, running both up and down and across the board, are embedded. Because the wires are arranged in this grid-like way, the points of intersection define specific horizontal and vertical co-ordinates.

Tracing and measuring is performed by a sensing cursor, which is hand-held and can be moved over the digitizing surface in a random manner. Inside the cursor is a coil, which generates an electromagnetic field and induces a signal at a specific co-ordinate in the matrix of wires embedded in the boards. Both the wire matrix and the cursor are linked to some form of data processing device, usually a computer.

Linear and rotary digitizers

Linear digitizers (op-tical displacement transducers) and rotary digitizers (optical shaft angle encoders) can be classified as either 'incremental' or 'absolute'.

Incremental digitizers produce a series of pulses while movement occurs (that is, while there is linear or rotary displacement). The greater the displacement the more pulses are produced. The speed of movement is determined from the pulse frequency (measured in pulses per second for example) and by summing or integrating these pulses the new position can be found.

A simple way to generate these pulses is to use the *moiré fringe effect*. Two sections of transparent material with closely spaced lines ruled across their surface are placed close together. One is fixed and the other attached to the moving member. These 'gratings' create a fringe pattern which moves when there is relative motion between the two gratings. By focusing a beam of light through the gratings at a PHOTOELECTRIC CELL the motion of these fringes can be detected—producing a series of electrical pulses.

Absolute encoders are a development of the incremental type and were developed mainly for the machine tool industry. The essential difference is that with the incremental type there is no immediate indication of absolute position, whereas with the absolute type this facility is provided.

Here, a binary coded multi-track scale with focused light beam and photoelectric cell produces the digital signal. The scale is quantized and each position is uniquely defined by its own binary number. Accuracy is improved by increasing the number of divisions on the scale, which means increasing the number of bits to describe each division.

Below : a rotary digitizer. This device gives information on the position of a rotating shaft in a digital form. In the sealed chamber to the left is housed an extremely accurate binary coded disc which is read by an optical device and converted to a usable digital form by the electronic circuitry mounted on the surrounding circuit boards. Resolutions down to 36 seconds of arc are possible.

Below : we can easily think and act in three dimensions because our world is three dimensional. Normally, a point in three dimensional space is represented by three numbers. These indicate the position of the point within three mutually perpendicular axes (co-ordinates).

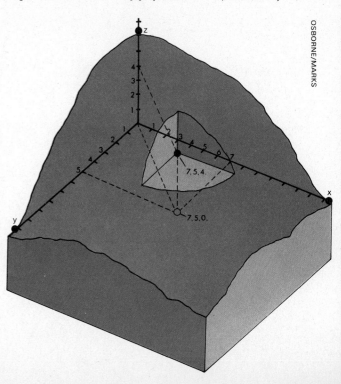

DIMENSIONS & dimensional analysis

We are no strangers to the idea of 'dimensions' as we use them every day. We see in three spatial, or length, dimensions and, with reference to real objects in the world around us, think in three dimensions. For example, to specify a location on the Earth's surface it is necessary to give the latitude, longitude and altitude above sea level. That is, three separate figures must be given to locate unambiguously a point on the Earth.

The definition of a dimension as it is used in physics and engineering is no more than an extension of the everyday meaning. A dimension is a generalization of the thing being measured.

Units and dimensions In our interpretation of the universe around us we assign numbers to the things we are considering (that is, we quantify them), but numbers alone are insufficient. We have to assign units as well.

For distance and length we talk about a number of feet or metres, miles or kilometres, but all units of distance have the dimension of length. The dimension here is the same as the thing being measured—namely length. When we quantify the mass of an object we measure it as a number of ounces or grammes, pounds or kilogrammes, but all these units have the dimension of mass. Similarly, we measure time in seconds minutes and so on, but they all have the dimension of time. The dimensions, mass and time, are the same as what is being measured—mass and time.

So far the idea of dimensions may seem to be rather trivial as they are no more than generalizations of what is being measured. Mass, length and time are, however, fundamental to all other physical quantities and form the basis of other, more complex, expressions.

Composite units and dimensions Because mass, length and time are so important they are called *primary properties* and from them composite properties are formed. For example, area has the units of square metres (m^2 or $m \times m$) or square miles ($mile^2$). The dimensions of area are therefore length squared and are written as $[L^2]$ (the square bracket means 'has the dimensions of'). Volume, for example in cubic feet or metres, has the dimensions of length cubed and is written as $[L^3]$.

Speed is the distance travelled (length) divided by the time taken to travel that distance, and is expressed in the composite units miles per hour ($mile/h$ or $mile \times h^{-1}$), metres per second (m/s or $m \times s^{-1}$) and so on. s^{-1} is a mathematical shorthand for $1/s^1$, while s^{-2} means $1/s^2$. Velocity therefore has the dimensions of $[L] [T^{-1}]$. Acceleration, which is the rate of change in velocity, is measured in such units as metres per second per second (m/s^2 or $m \times s^{-2}$) and therefore has the dimensions $[L] [T^{-2}]$.

Newton's second law of motion states that the magnitude of a force is found by multiplying the mass of the body that it acts on by the acceleration this force produces. Force therefore has the dimensions [mass] [acceleration]. Knowing the dimensions of acceleration we can represent force as $[M] [L] [T^{-2}]$.

Dimensional analysis The more complex the physical properties under consideration the more complex becomes the analysis of its dimensions. This can be seen by the extension from the three primary dimensions—mass M, length L and time T—to those of velocity, acceleration and force. Elementary dimensional analysis is often used to check that nothing has been omitted from a mathematical equation which expresses the relationship between one set of physical properties and another set. For example, there is a simple relation-ship between the velocity (v), wavelength (λ), and frequency (f) of sound or light waves. This is $v = \lambda f$. Wavelength has the dimension of length, $[L]$, frequency is the reciprocal of the time taken to travel one wavelength and therefore has the dimensions $[T^{-1}]$, and velocity is $[L] [T^{-1}]$. After replacing velocity, wavelength and frequency by their dimensions, the equation retains its integrity: $[L] [T^{-1}] = [L] \times [T^{-1}]$.

The more advanced techniques of dimensional analysis, such as those used by Albert Einstein to deduce the relationship between the electric and optical properties of matter, form an important part of the branch of science known as *mathematical physics*.

DIMMER SWITCH

A dimmer switch is a device included in an electrical circuit to regulate the amount of current flowing in that circuit. Frequently used in domestic and theatrical lighting, dimmer switches allow the amount of light produced by the circuit to be varied gradually from zero to full. There are three main types of dimming devices: the rheostat (see RESISTOR), the autotransformer, and the THYRISTOR. (None of these dimming devices can be used in a circuit with fluorescent lights (see DISCHARGE TUBES) without special circuitry to ensure that the voltage does not fall below the 'striking' voltage between the electrodes in the tube, for if it does, the gas in the tube will not be ionized and no light produced at all.)

Rheostat The earliest type of dimmer to be widely used, especially in the theatre, was the rheostat. This is simply a variable resistance wired into the circuit. A movable contact, usually with a dial face, enables any amount of resistance to be added to the circuit as desired. The higher the resistance the lower the current available to the filament in the light bulb. The nature of resistance means that some of the energy of the current will be dissipated in the form of heat. This means that a rheostat is not only wasteful of current but makes necessary some allowance for the heat, especially since it is likely to be generated in a confined place. For this reason, this type of dimmer is less widely used today.

Autotransformer A type of single coil transformer called an autotransformer is actually a voltage regulating device whose dimming characteristics are not dependent on load. A movable contact on the 'secondary' winding allows fractions of the mains current applied to the 'primary' to be tapped. This type of dimmer is used mainly for sensitive laboratory work.

An autotransformer dimmer switch has the added advantage of being able to produce a voltage on its secondary winding that is greater than that on its primary. Like an ordinary transformer, it is very efficient. It produces dimming in a similar way to the rheostat in that it passes a reduced current all the time, but self-induction entails nothing like the energy losses of the resistance in the rheostat.

Thyristor dimmer The development of the thyristor in the early 1950s revolutionized the technology of dimmer switches, among many others. The thyristor is an extension of the TRANSISTOR, being composed of four layers of crystal instead of the transistor's three.

As well as the common property of semiconductors of allowing current to pass through it in only one direction, the thyristor has the additional property of not allowing any current at all to pass unless a separate 'biasing' voltage is applied between two of its crystal layers.

The dimmer switch that exploits this characteristic consists of a circuit which includes two thyristors. The thyristors are wired to conduct current in opposite directions. In any half cycle of an alternating current, therefore, one thyristor will be passing current (provided the bias voltage is applied) and the other will not. In the other half of the cycle they change roles. The dimmer includes circuitry which draws the small bias voltage (about 5 volts) from the mains current, and includes a variable capacitance and resistance. Thus the point (or 'phase') at which the bias allows current to pass through the thyristor can be varied from the whole to zero. The part of the incoming half cycle applied to the thyristor before the required bias voltage is attained produces no current at all through the thyristor; this means that it is a far more efficient type of dimmer than the others, since it blocks the voltage rather than throwing part of it away. This also means that it can be designed very compactly, and the thyristor dimmer is widely used today, especially in domestic wiring.

Top right: the control panel of an electronic dimmer system for club and discothèque lighting, which can handle up to 2.5 kW.

Right: the inside of an electronic lighting controller. These units can control either tungsten lamps or fluorescent lighting.

Below: circuit of a rheostat dimmer switch. A sliding contact moves over a wire wound coil resistance from position 1—the off position, to 2 on zero resistance, light undimmed through 3 to 4—maximum resistance, minimum current for the dimmed light.

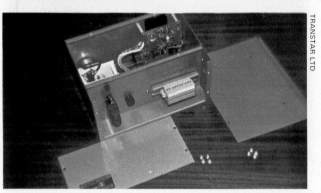

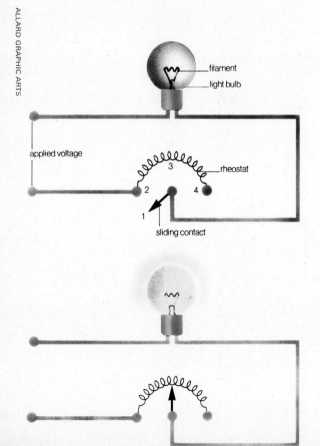

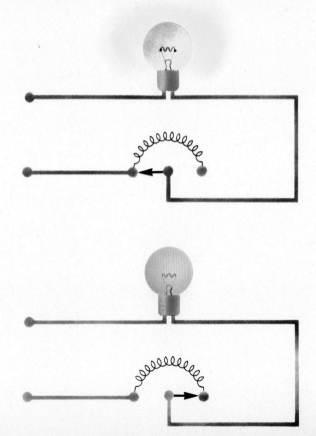

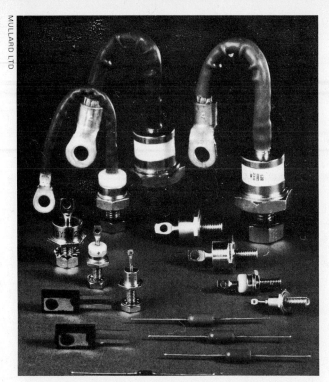

DIODE

A diode is either a VALVE [vacuum tube] or SEMICONDUCTOR device with two electrical terminals which permits current to flow between the terminals in one direction only. Diodes are found in a variety of ELECTRONIC circuits, but perhaps their most important application is in RECTIFIERS.

A rectifier is an electrical circuit for converting an AC power supply (that is, an ALTERNATING CURRENT source where the current flows first in one direction then in the other) to a DC power supply where the current flows in one direction only.

Valve diode The valve diode consists of two electrodes and a heating element sealed within an evacuated glass tube. One electrode, the cathode, is made from an ALKALI METAL, such as caesium, which readily boils off ELECTRONS when heated by the heating element which is close to it. (This is known as thermionic emission.) The other electrode, the anode, is made from a different metal from which electrons do not readily boil.

Left: a selection of semiconductor power diodes. The larger types have one terminal in the form of a lead and the other formed by the body.

Below: how a semiconductor diode works. Minority carriers (holes and electrons) can easily fall down the barrier 'slope' but the majority carriers cannot easily climb up the barrier. With no external voltage applied the number of minority carriers falling down the barrier equals the number of majority carriers climbing up and no nett current flows. With a reverse voltage the barrier is increased and fewer majority carriers climb the barrier and a small reverse current flows. With a forward voltage the barrier is reduced, more majority carriers overcome the barrier and a large forward current flows.

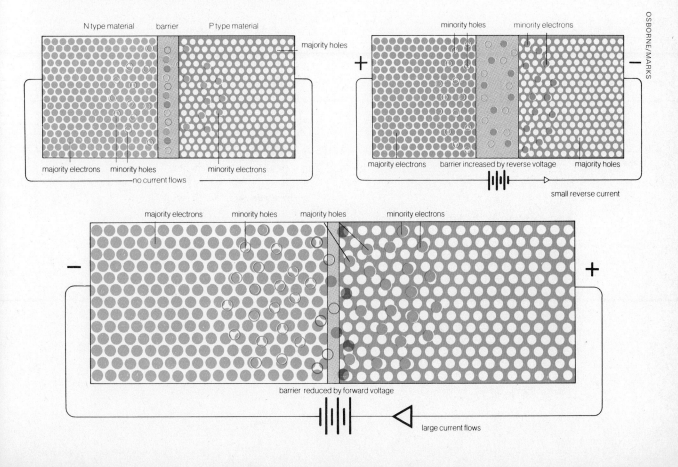

FERRANTI/PHOTO: PAUL BRIERLEY

When a voltage is applied between the anode and the cathode such that the anode is positive with respect to the cathode, electrons from the cathode are attracted towards the anode and current flows easily through the device. This is called the forward current direction, and the device is rather like a switch in the 'on' position. When, however, the voltage across the device is reversed, no current flows as there are no electrons available at the anode to constitute a current. In this case the diode exhibits an extremely high RESISTANCE and acts like a switch in the 'off' position. Today valve diodes have been largely replaced by semiconductors, except in certain industrial applications.

The semiconductor diode A semiconductor diode is made from silicon or germanium CRYSTALS. It consists of a thin slice of material cut from a single crystal which is alloyed on opposite surfaces with different material to give these areas of the crystal slightly different properties. One is called an n-type material because it results in an excess of electrons available for conduction ('n' for negative majority carriers). The other is called a p-type material because it has a number of 'vacancies' or holes, which can be filled by electrons. These holes constitute positive charges (equal and opposite to an electron—hence, p-type) and, like the electrons of the n-type material, they can move easily through the crystal lattice.

Inside the single crystal, between the p-type and n-type materials, is the p-n junction. Here there is neither a surfeit of electrons nor holes as some electrons from the n-type material diffuse across the junction and combine with holes of the p-type material, and some of the holes diffuse across the junction and combine with electrons. This region is called the *depletion layer,* as it is depleted of most of its electrons and holes.

The depletion layer behaves differently, electrically, to both the bulk of the n-type and p-type materials and is the region most responsible for the behaviour of the diode. This region is naturally a barrier to the movement of both holes and electrons. By analogy it presents a slope or gradient which only a few energetic holes and electrons can 'climb up', the rest falling back to their respective sides.

When the n-type region is made negative with respect to the p-type material by the application of a voltage (a forward voltage), this barrier is effectively reduced and more electrons and holes diffuse across the junction. The movement of these charges constitutes an electric current in the forward direction. When the voltage is reversed (a reverse voltage), however, the barrier is increased and only a minute reverse, or leakage, current flows.

DIRECT CURRENT (see electricity)

Top left: an array of light emitting diodes. These semiconductor devices are now widely used in many forms of displays, such as the numeric displays on electronic calculators. The light is emitted from the p-n junction of a gallium arsenide diode which has been treated with phosphorus to produce visible light. If phosphorus is not included in the semiconductor material the radiation emitted will be in the invisible infra-red region with a wavelength of between 900 and 950 nanometres (thousand millionths of a metre).

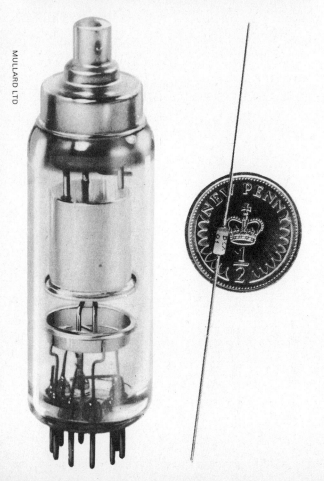

MULLARD LTD

Left: a valve (vacuum tube) diode (far left) and a miniature solid state diode (near left). The valve diode is designed for use as a high voltage rectifier in the picture tube circuit of a television receiver and operates at 20 kV. The semiconductor diode is a voltage reference or Zener diode, in which the resistance of the junction breaks down when a precise reverse voltage has been applied.

DISCHARGE TUBE

More than a century ago such workers as FARADAY, CROOKES and Thomson investigated the behaviour of sealed glass tubes containing electrodes connected to a supply of electric current. With air in the tube at atmospheric pressure no current could flow until the very high 'breakdown voltage' was reached, sufficient to ionize the gas between the electrodes, when a spark or arc could jump the gap (see CONDUCTION, ELECTRICAL). But if the pressure of the gas in the tube was reduced, interesting phenomena were observed. There were many variables, notably the shape of the tube, the distance between the electrodes, the voltage, the type of gas and its pressure. Out of this early research has come a very wide range of modern devices all of which are in the broadest sense discharge tubes. Among these devices are fluorescent lighting, STREET LIGHTING, CATHODE RAY TUBES (including TV, oscilloscope and radar displays), thermionic radio VALVES [vacuum tubes] and high intensity flashing lights.

Most gases are excellent insulators. For any current to flow there must be free electrons available. A very small number of such electrons are usually available as a result of ever-present cosmic or radioactive radiation, but the current these could support is barely measurable. As the applied voltage is increased the free electrons are eventually accelerated sufficiently to ionize other atoms of the gas by collision, resulting in the manufacture of additional carriers. When this occurs the current rapidly increases, while the applied voltage drops. If there is very low external resistance an arc could form between the electrodes, carrying a very large current over a fully ionized path with quite low voltage. In the usual discharge tube this is not allowed to occur.

Operation In the simplest form of discharge tube for laboratory demonstration, the electrodes are near each end of a glass tube connected to a vacuum pump, the potential between the electrodes being generated by an INDUCTION COIL with an output of about 10,000 volts. At atmospheric pressure, with air or other gas, the current is of the order of microamperes, but when the pressure is reduced to below about $1/15$ atmospheric a current flows and the electrodes are joined by irregular, unstable streams of ionized gas which glow visibly. As the pressure falls further the streamers strengthen, coalesce and instead of following erratic paths adopt a stable pattern. They fill most of the space between the electrodes, their colour being characteristic of the gas (for example, pink for air, reddish for nitrogen, and bright red for neon).

At a pressure of about $1/10,000$ atmospheric there is a glow at each electrode, a negative glow around the cathode (separated from it by the 'Crookes dark space') and a glowing positive column filling most of the tube which is increasingly striated into dark and light transverse bands. The positive column is separated from the cathode glow by the 'Faraday dark space'. This becomes larger as pressure is further reduced. At about $1/100,000$ atmospheric pressure the positive column has disappeared into the anode, and the tube is dark (because there are hardly any gas atoms to be ionized). Yet the cathode still glows, and a new glow arises from the glass at the other end of the tube, due to bombardment by *cathode rays*. The energy of these rays depends on the applied voltage, and in radar and TV screens they fall on a screen on the end of the tube facing the cathode, which is coated with a *phosphor* (a chemical which fluoresces).

Before about 1940 the most common discharge tubes were thermionic valves [vacuum tubes]. In these the interior is evacuated to a very low pressure indeed, and there are usually more than two electrodes (anode and cathode). In a triode a grid is interposed, and in some tubes there are as many as 12 electrodes. The purpose of the tube is normally to amplify or in some other way control or alter a flow of current as part of an electronic or electrical circuit. Most such tubes are, or were, used to control very small currents but thyratrons and ignitrons are still used in heavy electric power engineering. In electronics the vacuum or gas filled tube has been largely superseded by the TRANSISTOR and other devices based on SEMICONDUCTORS.

Fluorescent tubes Today the most important discharge tube is probably the fluorescent light. The type most commonly used for illumination is a slender glass tube filled with mercury vapour at low pressure, with argon added to help the starting. Mercury is liquid at normal temperatures, so the discharge begins in the argon, which heats the tube and the mercury, which vaporizes.

At each end is a filament-type electrode coated with a material which readily emits electrons when heated. When the current—usually ALTERNATING CURRENT—is switched on, the filaments heat up and emit electrons, each one acting as the

An 1857 discharge tube experiment by Alexandre Becquerel, father of the man who discovered radioactivity. He put various materials into a discharge tube to observe their fluorescence—in this case, it is Willemite, Zn_2SiO_4.

anode or cathode depending on the half-cycle of the current. A high voltage between the electrodes is needed to start the argon discharge, and this is done by using a *starter* and a *choke* or *ballast*. The starter automatically breaks the circuit when the filaments have heated up, causing the choke, which is an induction coil, to produce a brief pulse of high voltage electricity. This starts the argon discharge and, very shortly, a mercury discharge. This is self-sustaining, with a continuous flow of electrons between the electrodes.

The radiation from the ionized vapour is strong in ultra-violet. This falls on a coating of fluorescent material on the inside of the tube, which glows by absorbing the invisible and harmful ultra-violet and re-radiating it as visible light. The colour of this light can be chosen by suitably arranging the the mix of the fluorescent coating, the most common shades being white or 'warm white'.

Fluorescent lights operate at a much lower temperature than normal light bulbs. As more of the electrical energy goes into emitting light, and less into heat, these lamps are relatively efficient, and an 80 watt tube provides the same light output as four 100 W filament bulbs.

Because of the relatively high current needed to start the tube, and because the filaments have a coating with a limited life, it is not advisable to switch fluorescent lights on and off frequently, or much of their economy will be lost. Indeed, it is the exhaustion of the oxide coatings on the filaments which causes a tube to ultimately fail, unless the starting circuit has broken down.

Streetlights
Most streetlights are discharge tubes of one sort or another. Those most frequently used are sodium, which gives a yellow-orange light, and mercury, with a blue-green light.

Sodium vapour lamps are usually of the low-pressure kind —the gas in the tube is mostly neon at about one hundredth atmospheric pressure. When the lamp is not lit, the sodium is not in the vapour form—it is a solid when below 208 °F (98 °C). Neon, however, will sustain a discharge at lower temperatures, though it does not give very much illumination. But it is sufficient to heat the tube up so that the sodium vaporizes and glows with its characteristic light—the total warm up time is about 8 to 15 minutes.

Sodium vapour light consists almost completely of one wavelength only (more accurately, a pair of closely-spaced wavelengths). This *monochromatic* light is luckily at about the peak colour sensitivity of the eye, so for efficient streetlighting it is ideal. But colour vision is impossible in such a light, so high pressure lamps are becoming used in city centres and similar locations. These are operated at a higher power loading so that the temperature and vapour pressure are increased. This produces glows of a range of colours on either side of the yellow part of the spectrum. The light from these lamps appears much whiter.

Sodium vapour is very reactive, and attacks ordinary soda-lime glass. The envelope of the lamp therefore has a lining of glass with a low silica content, which can resist hot sodium.

Mercury vapour lamps operate at a high pressure compared with sodium lamps, about one atmosphere, though the pressure is not so high to start with. Argon is used to help start the discharge since mercury is liquid when cold: in addition, an auxiliary starting electrode close to a main electrode sets the discharge going and heats the tube. The mercury vaporizes, and the mercury discharge begins. Warm-up time to full output is about 5 minutes. If the electricity supply is interrupted,

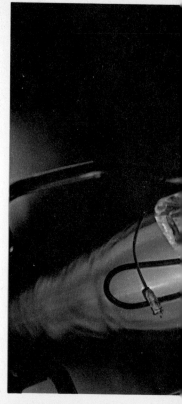

Right: a metal iodide lamp. The photograph has been deliberately underexposed so that the details of the discharge itself can be seen. There is a central core joining the electrodes, with the glow becoming more and more diffuse further away. The yellow drops are due to iodide which has not completely vaporized.

Below: the early discharge tubes were called Geissler tubes, after their German inventor. These examples show the variety of forms which the discharge can take. The gas in this case is probably air; the tube on the left shows the striations produced at low pressure. The dark patch above the striations is the Faraday dark space; above this is the blue negative glow, with the Crookes dark space between that and the electrode. Geissler tubes were produced in a variety of shapes using different gases, as novelties, shown at bottom right.

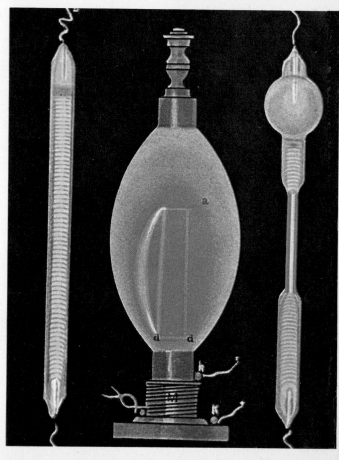

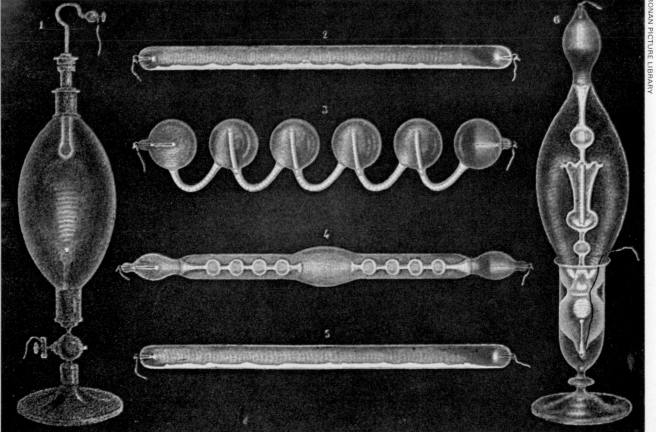

however, the lamp goes off and has to cool down until the vapour pressure falls to a suitable value for restarting.

The mercury lamp gives a greenish-blue colour, lacking red. To overcome this, a fluorescent coating can be given to the inside of the tube—this absorbs unwanted ultra-violet and re-radiates it as red light. These lamps differ from ordinary fluorescent tubes in that they are at high, rather than low pressure. Low pressure tubes rely on the fluorescence to produce light, whereas high pressure ones are just corrected for colour by the fluorescent material.

The colour and efficiency of high power high pressure mercury lamps can also be improved by adding a small amount of another metal in the form of a halide (that is, in combination with a HALOGEN.) Sodium iodide and mercury iodide are used in this way for floodlights, and are invariably used to light stadiums to the level required for colour television.

Other types   Mercury vapour tubes are often the basis of ULTRA-VIOLET LAMPS, without a fluorescent coating, and using a glass which does not absorb ultra-violet.

Other kinds of discharge tube are designed to emit discrete flashes of light of very high intensity. They may be used as flashing beacons on aircraft, in lighthouses, for FLASHGUNS, and for pumping LASERS. Xenon is a common gas used for these devices; the high discharge voltage is supplied by charging up a CAPACITOR.

The QUARTZ-HALOGEN bulb, widely used for car headlights and projector bulbs, is not a discharge tube but a tungsten filament lamp operating at very high temperature in iodine vapour.

Piccadilly Circus, London. The famous display signs, popularly known as neon tubes, are actually not neon filled in many cases. Neon gives an orange-red glow, but the wide range of colours available in signs is produced by fluorescent tubes filled with argon and mercury. The fluorescent powder, combined with coloured glass for the tube, can produce almost any colour. The electrodes are not heated, as in the household tube, so about 2000 V is needed to start the discharge off.

DISHWASHING MACHINE

The first dishwashing machines, designed for restaurants and caterers, generally worked on the principle of passing the dirty crockery under jets of hot water by means of a conveyer belt or a revolving basket. Modern dishwashers have reversed this procedure, the stationary ware being washed by revolving jets above and below the basket.

A typical dishwasher is housed in an enamelled cabinet designed to match and complement other large kitchen appliances. A drop-down door enables the plastic coated crockery basket to be pulled out on slides or rollers for loading. The door is fitted with a microswitch to shut off all operations if the door is opened during a cycle. The interior of the machine is finished in stainless steel, plastic coated steel or vitreous enamel.

Water supply   The water connections for the machine can consist of a hose connection from an existing tap, or they can be plumbed in permanently. Most machines only take cold water, since they have their own heating elements. Waste water is removed by a pump via a drain hose. If the drain hose is plumbed in permanently, it must be done at the correct height in order to prevent accidental siphoning of the wash water out of the machine. As an additional precaution against siphoning, the waste pipe can be vented to the atmosphere by means of an air hole.

The amount of water used varies from less than three Imperial gallons (3.6 US gallons, 13 litres) to 24 Imperial gallons (29 US gallons, 110 litres), depending on the size of the machine and the wash cycle selected. (Ordinary domestic machines are at the low end of this scale.) The temperature of the water is from 60° to 70°C (140° to 158°F), much hotter than hands can bear.

Heater, pumps and motors   The heater rating can be from 1800 to 2750W. Heaters are normally of the mineral insulated sheathed element type, consisting of a heating spiral contained in a metal tube but insulated from it. The insulation is typically made of compacted magnesium oxide powder. This type of element can be safely immersed in water; its operation is controlled by a THERMOSTAT.

Dishwashing machines have separate vane pumps to provide water pressure to the spray arms and to remove the dirty water. Some machines have one motor to operate both pumps, but most have separate motors. The motors are protected by overload cutouts embedded in the windings to shut them off if they overheat.

Dishwashers are electrically earthed, usually by fitting a 2-pole and earth plug.

Operation A dishwasher generally has several programmes which may be selected by means of keys or push buttons, depending on the type of utensils to be washed and the type of food residues to be removed. A typical programme begins with a cool or warm rinse, continues with a hot wash with detergent, and concludes with several rinses. The rinse may include a rinse aid, which is essentially a wetting solution, and the final rinse will be hot, to aid drying. Some machines dry the dishes by means of heat, using the heating element as a heat source.

The wash and rinse water is sprayed from above and below the dish basket by whirling arms through which the water is pumped; each of the arms has several spray holes in it. The detergent and the rinse aid are stored in dispensers which automatically release the right amount at the proper point in the cycle. The machine usually has a built-in water softener, to to which salt must be periodically added.

A timing device automatically controls the selected cycle; it is often operated by means of a round calibrated knob. Turning it in one direction starts the cycle and it turns back slowly as the machine operates. Some machines have pilot lights which indicate which part of the cycle is currently in operation. Sometimes the knob has a push-pull off-on function so that the cycle can be stopped at any time to put in or take out utensils.

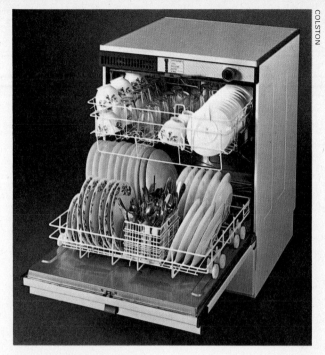

COLSTON

Above right: a modern dishwasher fully loaded. A whole day's dishes can be washed in one load.

Right: a cutaway view of a dishwasher, with one loading tray removed for easy viewing. The revolving spray arms can be seen at top and bottom. Pumps and motors are installed in the bottom of the machine; controls and detergent dispenser are located in the door. This dishwasher has a thermal drying feature: hot air is circulated by a fan and moisture is condensed out of it. The machine also filters the water and recycles it, saving water and money. The inside of the machine is finished in stainless steel.

Left: a heavy duty dishwashing installation. This is a conveyer design which can be fitted for gas, electric or steam heat. Panels at the bottom front are removable for easy servicing of pumps and motors. The stainless steel spray baskets have moulded polypropylene nozzles and stainless steel mesh strainer baskets which slide out for easy cleaning. The equipment is installed at table-top height to keep lifting at a minimum.

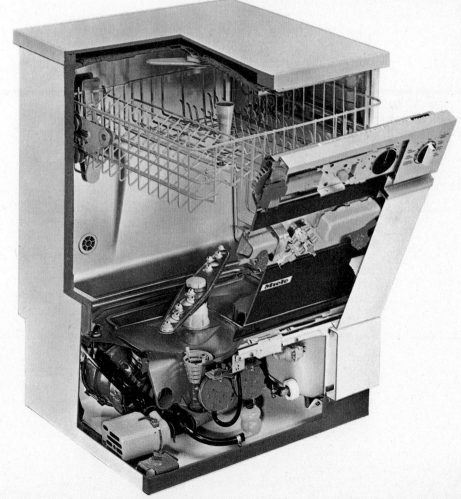

MIELE CO LTD

DISTANCE RECORDER

The distance recorder, odometer or hodometer, provides a means of recording distances traversed over land or sea. It is a COUNTING DEVICE operated by a vehicle's movement.

The vehicle odometer, usually driven by a flexible cable from the gearbox or another part of the drive transmission system, is familiar to all drivers. Many cyclists, also, fit a 'cyclometer', operated by a lug attached to one of the spokes of the front wheel. A sea going vessel may carry a 'patent log', which is simply an odometer mounted on a stern rail and driven by a small impeller at the end of a long cable, which is rotated by the forward motion of the vessel. Alternatively, the impeller may be fixed beneath the hull.

The odometer records only in units, which may be feet, yards, metres, kilometres or miles, or in tenth or hundredth parts of these units. The gearing between the prime mover and the drive shaft of the counter must be extremely accurate, and if the prime mover is changed the odometer must be re-calibrated.

The counting device itself has normally 6, 7, 8 or more light-weight, low torque drums each bearing the figures 0 to 9. The drums, mounted on a common shaft, rotate independently but are linked by an intermittent motion mechanism. The first, right hand, drum is driven directly by the input shaft or its equivalent. As this first wheel completes the last tenth of its first turn, a single gear tooth on its side engages a 'starwheel' pinion gear mounted between the first and second drums. This pinion is permanently engaged with a continuous gear on the 'driven' side of the second drum. Thus the second drum follows the first at a 1:1 speed ratio for 36° or 1/10 of a revolution, moving the next numeral into place. After ten such partial revolutions of the second drum, the third is similarly turned through 36° as the counter moves from 99 to 100, and so on.

Some odometers include a second counter with fewer drums recording perhaps only four figures. This second set—the'trip' meter, for recording relatively short A to B distances—is driven by a 1:1 ratio gear off the main shaft, so that both the main and trip meters record at the same time. The trip meter can be manually reset to zero when required, spring detents (catches) being used to hold the drums lightly at zero.

The odometer can also be operated by electrical pulses generated by switches, photocells, magnetic pickups or relays as the distance is traversed. The pulses are converted into mechanical motion by a solenoid operating a pawl and ratchet device on the first drum of the counter. Where a permanent record is required, the electrical pulses can be employed to deflect a pen marking a renewable chart, so that a count of the number of deflections on the chart corresponds to the number of units traversed.

For survey work the odometer, also known as a perambulator or ambulator, is mounted on a frame attached to a large wheel, up to 6 ft (2 m) in diameter; this is attached at its axis to a handle so that it may be wheeled over the distance to be measured. The reason for the large diameter is so that the wheel can ride smoothly over hollows and bumps in the ground, for in surveying all linear distances assume that the surface is perfectly flat. Over smooth surfaces, therefore, such as pavements or floors, the perambulator wheel may be as small as one foot (30 cm) in diameter. The perambulator is sometimes towed behind a vehicle, as in performance testing. For measuring the size of a room, for example, the surveyor uses a small perambulator on the end of a stick.

Below: one of the most common uses of distance recorders is to measure car performance. The wheel is connected to a purpose-built odometer inside the car.

'MOTOR'

DISTILLATION

Distillation plays an important part in the production of petrol [gasoline], whisky, drinking water (see DESALINATION), fragrant oils and oxygen. It is one of the most widely used separation techniques in both industry and the research laboratory.

Distillation is very similar to evaporation; both depend on molecules of a liquid escaping from the surface and forming a vapour or gas. In evaporation, the vapour is dispersed and the residue, which is left behind, is collected; while in distillation the vapour is subsequently cooled and condenses as a liquid which is collected. The tendency of a liquid to become a vapour is called the *vapour pressure* and is dependent on the temperature. Molecules in a liquid have to escape from the surface to form a vapour, and the ease with which they can do this depends on the intermolecular attraction, the mass of the molecule and its velocity. As the temperature increases so will the average velocity of the liquid molecules. On heating to the boiling point there are sufficient molecules with velocities high enough to overcome the intermolecular forces, and bubbles of vapour form throughout the liquid; in other words, it boils. At the boiling point the vapour pressure of the liquid equals the pressure of the surrounding air, that is, atmospheric pressure. At temperatures below the boiling point, only a few surface molecules can escape, while molecules in the body of the liquid lose energy by collisions with neighbouring molecules and their average velocity is insufficient to cause boiling.

History The first mention of distillation seems to have been by Aristotle (384–322 BC), when he described sea water being evaporated to make drinking water. The Romans and Alexandrians (from Alexandria, Egypt) distilled pine-wood resin to condense the oil of turpentine ('turps') which boiled off. These processes used air-cooled condensing arms (outlet from the boiling vessel), which allowed the most volatile components to escape. It was probably the Arabians who first used a water-cooled arm, and using this method they discovered various essential oils (natural plant oils, used mostly as flavourings or perfumes) by distilling plant juices. Later the alchemists, using a distillation apparatus known as an *alembic*, were able to prepare relatively pure nitric acid and other mineral acids.

The preparation of alcoholic beverages by distillation has taken place since antiquity. Distilled alcohol, probably discovered in Italy in the early twelfth century, was at first used as a medicine. The apothecaries and monasteries possessed stills

Bottom left: an early 16th century example of fractional distillation. The stills at the bottom were heated by hot ashes, represented by the artist as flames. The vapours passed up a system of interlocking condensing tubes which passed in and out of a water tower, being cooled by air and water, before condensing into the receivers above.

Bottom right: a 210 ft (64 m) crude oil distillation column dominates this modern refinery complex.

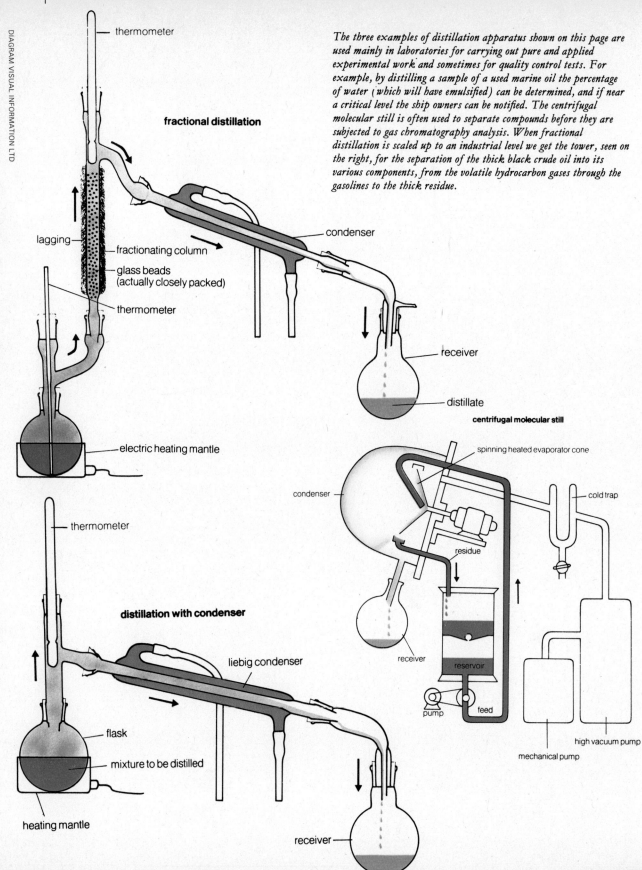

thermometer

fractional distillation

The three examples of distillation apparatus shown on this page are used mainly in laboratories for carrying out pure and applied experimental work and sometimes for quality control tests. For example, by distilling a sample of a used marine oil the percentage of water (which will have emulsified) can be determined, and if near a critical level the ship owners can be notified. The centrifugal molecular still is often used to separate compounds before they are subjected to gas chromatography analysis. When fractional distillation is scaled up to an industrial level we get the tower, seen on the right, for the separation of the thick black crude oil into its various components, from the volatile hydrocarbon gases through the gasolines to the thick residue.

lagging

fractionating column

glass beads
(actually closely packed)

thermometer

condenser

receiver

distillate

electric heating mantle

centrifugal molecular still

spinning heated evaporator cone

condenser

cold trap

residue

receiver

reservoir

pump

feed

high vacuum pump

mechanical pump

thermometer

distillation with condenser

liebig condenser

flask

mixture to be distilled

heating mantle

receiver

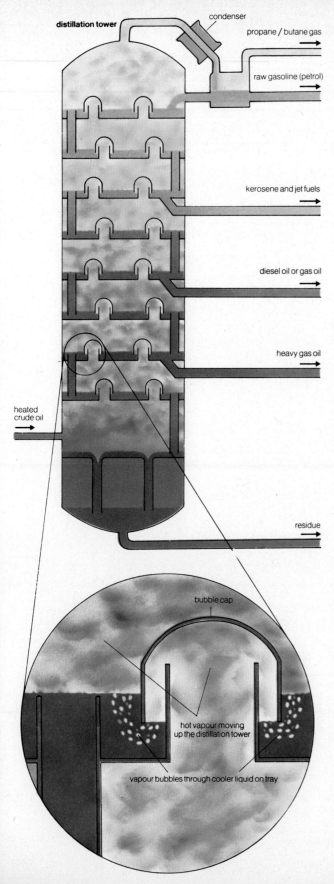

distillation tower

condenser

propane / butane gas

raw gasoline (petrol)

kerosene and jet fuels

diesel oil or gas oil

heavy gas oil

heated crude oil

residue

bubble cap

hot vapour moving up the distillation tower

vapour bubbles through cooler liquid on tray

and sometimes mixed the alcohol they distilled with herbs and spices. It was from these early medicinal experiments that liqueurs such as Benedictine and Chartreuse were developed. Wine was distilled to make brandy, whisky was made from fermented barley grain (malt) mashes, rum from fermented cane sugar, vodka from rye or potatoes, gin was alcohol from various sources flavoured with juniper berries and angostura bitters. By the early 1800s large-scale distilleries had been developed similar to those in use today.

Straight distillation The simplest arrangement for a distillation apparatus is a still or retort in which the liquid is heated, and a condenser which condenses the vapour and takes the liquid formed into a receiving vessel. Such simple apparatus is only used to separate a liquid from a solid or to separate liquids which have very different boiling points. Simple distillation is used in Kuwait to make drinking water from sea water; the natural gas from the adjacent oil fields is used to provide the heating required, a very cheap form of energy in that locality.

In laboratory work a type of condenser made from glass, known as a Liebig condenser, is generally used. It is a long tube surrounded by a water jacket through which cold water is continually circulated.

Fractional distillation If the boiling points of two liquids in a mixture are close, a poor separation is obtained by using the simple still. By separating the still head from the still pot with a column, much better separation occurs. This is because a temperature gradient (that is a decrease of temperature with distance) is established between the hotter pot and cooler head. As the vapour rises up the column it begins to condense because of the cooling effect of the air surrounding the column, and this liquid then drops back into the pot—a process called refluxing. At each point up the column the descending liquid is in contact with the rising vapour. Gradually the vapour becomes richer in the more volatile components (substances with lower boiling points) as the less volatile fractions condense out. The remaining liquid becomes more concentrated in the less volatile components.

The efficiency of this process depends on the vapour and liquid in the column always being in intimate contact with each other. In the laboratory the columns are usually packed with small objects. These may be glass, ceramic or metal and come in all shapes: beads, spheres, rings and small hollow cylinders. The columns may also be of different sizes and shapes. All of the variations attempt to maximize the vapour-liquid contact and this increases the efficiency of the fractionation.

Industrial-scale columns are not packed because it was found that the liquid tended to form channels and flow down these, thereby avoiding the vapour. Various designs are currently used but all of these depend on the column being split by horizontal plates. The vapour bubbles through holes in these plates and the liquid flows down from one to the other. Sieves with small disc valves over each hole or perforated bubble caps ensure thorough mixing as the vapour passes through the liquid.

In the laboratory the fractions are collected from the head and passed through a condenser to a receiving vessel. As the distillation continues the temperature of the head increases as the more volatile portions are collected. This is a batch process and is usually operated on a small scale. Industrially, the distillation needs to be continuous. The OIL industry uses fractional distillation to separate different products from crude oil.

The crude oil is fed into a column at about one-third the way up. At the bottom, vapour is produced by heating up the residue with steam, and at the top a reflux (that is a recycling condenser) returns some of the condensed vapour. As soon as the whole column is in equilibrium it is tapped at various heights and liquids are taken off by controlling outlet valves. The top end has the most volatile components, the gases, the raw gasoline and raw kerosine; the middle of the column produces the gas oils and the bottom, the fuel oils. The residue is often passed to a vacuum distillation unit to make lubricants. These different components are collected and then blended to make the final products.

Fractional distillation is so effective that liquefied air may be separated not only to produce oxygen and nitrogen but also the inert gases argon, neon, krypton and xenon which may be recovered in commercial quantities.

One of the problems of fractionation of liquids is the formation of constant boiling point mixtures known as *azeotropes* that distil over without change in composition (their boiling point is lower or higher than any of the components). One example of an azeotrope is rectified spirit which consists of 95% ethyl alcohol and 5% water. In order to obtain pure alcohol, a third component, benzene, must be added which then distils over with all the water, leaving anhydrous alcohol.

Steam distillation This technique is used to distil organic compounds which are immiscible with water and have an appreciable vapour pressure at 100 °C (the boiling point of water), and are also liable to decompose or oxidize at their own higher boiling point. Aniline is a well known example. Steam is passed into the organic and water layers causing the mixture to boil and distil over in approximate proportion to their vapour pressures. The purified organic layer is then separated.

Distillation under reduced pressure Compounds having large molecules generally boil at high temperatures, but at temperatures above 350 °C (572 °F) they are liable to decompose.

One way to avoid excessive heat is steam distillation (discussed above); another way is to reduce the pressure within the apparatus and lower the boiling temperature to which the substance is subjected. This permits high boiling substances to be distilled without decomposition. The whole system is sealed off from the atmosphere and the pressure is reduced by an evacuating pump, pressure down to 10^{-6} mm (atmospheric pressure is 760 mm) of mercury are used for laboratory experiments.

Reduced pressure, or *vacuum distillation* as it is called, is used to distil the residue from the crude oil fractionation to produce high viscosity oils used as lubricating oils; the residue in this case is BITUMEN [asphalt], used for surfacing roads. Vacuum distillation is also used to remove the unpleasant odours from oils such as cotton seed and soya bean to make them suitable for cooking.

Molecular distillation When the materials are either extremely sensitive to heat and cannot be heated to their normal boiling points or are readily oxidized by the oxygen in the air if heated in contact with it, then molecular distillation is often used. At pressures of 0.001 mm of mercury or less this type of distillation can be carried out at low temperatures. It is particularly

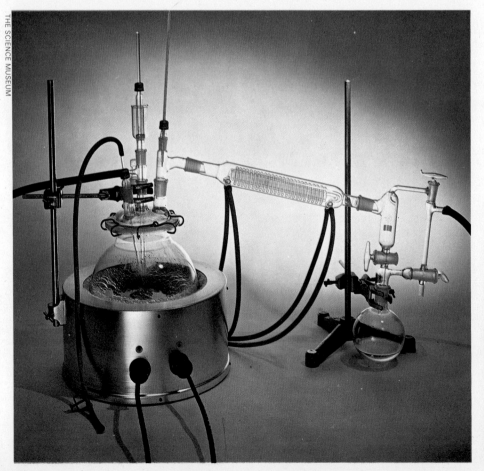

useful for distilling compounds of high molecular weight, say in the range of 500 to 1000. This covers many complex organic molecules that occur naturally. The method really involves an evaporation of the liquid on to a closely situated cooled receiver, and depends solely on the molecule getting up enough speed to escape from the surface of the liquid and hit the condensing surface. Therefore distillation no longer depends on the vapour pressure of the liquid equalling that of the surrounding atmosphere.

Because molecular distillation occurs only from the surface of the liquid and not throughout the liquid (as normally) it is best to have as large a surface as possible. One way of doing this is to feed the material for distillation on to a hot rotating cone which is contained in a dome-shaped chamber. This chamber is kept at a very reduced pressure. Centrifugal forces spread the mixture over the hot surface and any volatile material quickly evaporates off and is collected in the cooled domed condenser and then flows into a receiving vessel. The residue is spun off and can be returned to the input. Any heat-sensitive material therefore remains in contact with the hot surface for only a very short time, so this method is extremely effective.

Bottom left: modern glassware for carrying out a laboratory distillation under reduced pressure. The still is heated in a thermostatically controlled electric heating mantle.

Bottom right: the stillhouse at a typical Highland malt whisky distillery. Malt whisky is distilled twice.

DISTRIBUTOR

The operation of the INTERNAL COMBUSTION ENGINE, used in most cars, depends on each of the SPARK PLUGS in the cylinders receiving a pulse of high voltage (or high tension, HT) electricity at precisely the right moment in order to spark off the fuel-air mixture. The HT is produced by an INDUCTION COIL from the low voltage (low tension, LT) provided by the car battery. The spark must come at the correct stage in the cylinder and valve operation (that is, the *timing* should be right), and the order in which the pulses are distributed to the spark plugs should be right. The device which regulates all this is the distributor.

Before distributors were developed, *magnetos* were used. These are small generators for producing high voltages using a permanent magnet and no battery, but they were expensive and sometimes unreliable. A new system had to be found; hence the development of the distributor, which came into general use in the 1940s.

Components
The conventional distributor is quite a compact unit, housed in a cylindrical aluminium casing about 1 inch (2.5 cm) across at the bottom end, belling out from the middle upwards to about 3 inch (7.6 cm) across. A typical unit is about 7 inch (18 cm) long, and is clamped to the side of the cylinder block, so that it can tap the rotary motion of the CAM-SHAFT. This is the shaft which operates the pushrods to open and close the valves, rotating once for every firing sequence of the engine. This connection therefore mechanically locks the movement of a central drive spindle in the distributor to the motion of the engine, and changes in the timing can be made by rotating the body of the distributor around this spindle.

As the spindle turns, a rotor arm at its top end points towards a contact for each cylinder in turn, acting as a rotary switch. At the same time, a raised edge on a CAM on the spindle separates a pair of contacts in the low tension circuit, so producing the spark. There are as many raised edges around the spindle as there are cylinders.

Ignition circuit
A voltage of some 30,000 V is needed for a good spark. The induction coil provides this from the low tension (usually 12 V) supply from the battery: every time the LT supply is cut off, a spark is produced. LT current is therefore supplied to the *contact breaker* assembly continuously; the supply is interrupted as the spindle turns, and is fed to the coil. This produces an HT pulse for every break of the contacts. The pulses then pass along a single lead to the centre of the rotor arm, which distributes them to the cylinder contacts in the right order. The rotor does not need to actually touch each contact—this would result in rapid wear—but the gap is so small that the pulse can easily jump across with very little reduction in voltage. The central contact is provided by a spring loaded carbon rod which can both carry high voltage and form a low friction connection with the moving rotor arm, which has a brass plate mounted on a Bakelite cap to insulate it from the drive spindle.

Contact breaker
The contact breaker assembly is mounted on a flat plate which fits into the distributor body over the drive spindle, and can thus be replaced when the 'points' or contacts become worn. One contact is fixed to the plate, while the other is moved by the cam follower, which thus separates the contact points, once for every edge on the cam of the drive spindle.

A means of adjustment for the maximum of the points must be provided, since this affects the duration of the spark and therefore the running of the engine. A CAPACITOR (condenser) connected across the points acts as a reservoir of electricity to prevent small sparks jumping when the points are open.

Timing The other important adjustment necessary on a distributor is the timing. This can be altered coarsely by twisting the distributor body around the drive spindle, and more precisely by a screw thread which does the same job once the approximate position has been set.

As the engine speeds up, the ignition should be *advanced* for optimum running—that is, the spark should occur slightly earlier in the cylinder operation. An automatic advance mechanism is usually provided, using the vacuum which occurs in the inlet manifold of the carburettor as the accelerator is pressed down and more air is sucked in. A small pipe connects this to a diaphragm which moves in and out as the vacuum changes. The movement of this diaphragm pulls the base plate, giving more or less advance to the timing. This device depends upon the accelerator setting rather than the engine speed and has most effect at half throttle, when the engine is not at full

Below : a cutaway model of a modern distributor. The white and black wire is the low tension lead, which runs through the side of the body and is connected to the contact breaker. The capacitor and rotor can be seen next to the points, and the vacuum advance diaphragm is inside the polished cover at the top of the picture.

speed. To allow for changes in engine speed, the cam is carried on a sleeve which fits over the drive spindle, linked by balance (bob) weights and springs. As the engine speed increases, centrifugal force throws the weights outwards, causing the points to open sooner.

Insulation The various components of a distributor which are not supposed to be at the earth voltage of the chassis have to be well insulated. In the case of the LT, small washers are adequate. The HT, however, can easily jump small gaps so the distributor cover is usually made of a good insulator such as Bakelite. A good seal against water is important, and a rubber or plastic cover over the whole unit is often advisable. It is not uncommon for tracks of carbon to form on the inside of the distributor cover or the rotor arm as a result of moisture. These can reduce the spark voltage and even stop the car if allowed to build up.

Latest developments On modern high performance cars electronic ignition systems are used, these being much more expensive than the mechanical system, but more precise in the timing. The contact points are done away with and coils are used instead. As one coil rotates around in the distributor, the other remains fixed to the base plate. When one moves over the other a pulse is sent down the line to electronic circuits which develop and distribute a very high voltage to each plug in turn.

DIVING BELL

The diving bell is the oldest and simplest piece of diving equipment. Its principle can be demonstrated with a tumbler in the kitchen sink. If the sink is filled with water and the tumbler pushed upside-down to the bottom, the inside of the tumbler will stay dry because of the air trapped in it. The diving bell is simply a large 'cup' lowered from a ship with a man inside it.

In practice it is not quite that simple, for two reasons. First of all, air is compressible, which means that the deeper the bell goes the 'wetter' the inside of it will get. For example, at a depth of 10 m the pressure of the water surrounding the bell will be twice the air pressure inside it, which means that the bell will be half full of water. Secondly, the bell is inclined to be buoyant, on account of the air inside it. It must therefore be very heavy or it must have weights attached to it, to enable it to sink and to remain upright.

History The first recorded use of the principle of a diving bell is by Aristotle, in his *Problematum* (fourth century BC). He

Left: a thirteenth century manuscript illustration of Alexander the Great, who is said to have descended in a diving bell out of curiosity. There are several versions of the story.

Below: an 1857 model; apparently very buoyant, it had an entry hatch on the top and was supplied with air pumped from the surface.

describes a device shaped like a bucket lowered upside-down to divers to breathe from. An early French manuscript shows Alexander the Great underwater, in a glass barrel lit with candles. This illustration shows a lot of artistic licence: there were probably no glass barrels in Alexander's time, and candles would use up the air in the bell rather quickly.

During the 1530s, an enterprising Italian named Guglielmo de Lorena dived to the bottom of Lake Neni, a water-filled crater in the Alban hills, to examine two Roman galleys known to have sunk there. De Lorena's bell was fitted with a window. Then in 1538, two Greeks designed and built a diving bell large enough for two divers. It was demonstrated in Toledo, Spain, before the Emperor Charles V and several thousand other spectators. In this case a single candle was used, and it was still burning when the diving bell was brought to the surface. Following the success of the Greeks' device, the Spanish used diving bells extensively: in 1665 divers recovered guns from a Spanish ship wrecked in 1588, and in 1677 a wooden bell 13 ft high and 10 ft in diameter (4 m × 3 m) was used to recover money from shipwrecks.

In the meantime, in the early 1600s an Englishman, Richard Norwood, was looking for shipwrecks near Bermuda, using an inverted wine barrel with weights attached. A similar device was described by Sir Francis Bacon in 1620. One hundred years later, Dr Edmund Halley (of Halley's Comet fame) devised a system of supplying air to divers. Halley's bell was large, with a capacity exceeding 60 ft³ (1.70 m³), and was made of wood with a lead covering and glass portholes. Empty lead casks were lowered to the bell; the divers would pull the casks under the bell, pull out the bungs and fresh air would burble in, pushing some of the water out.

Before that, in 1689, a French physicist, Dr Denis Papin, was the first to pump air through a tube down to divers in a bell. Later pumps were more powerful, allowing divers to work at greater depths, and the lines were fitted with one-way valves, so that if the pumps failed the air could not be forced through the line up to the surface by the water pressure around the bell, flooding it. By the early nineteenth century, the diving bell had graduated from being a curiosity or a tool of treasure hunters to the status of a workmanlike apparatus. In 1823, however, with the patent of the first diving helmet, the technology of diving equipment began to make the bell obsolete. During the nineteenth century every harbour of any size had a diving bell for routine work on ships and breakwater, but today applications of the diving bell are limited.

The principle of the diving bell, however, is receiving a new lease on its usefulness on account of present-day research into fish farming, as well as other techniques of cultivation and mineral research at the bottom of the sea. The old-fashioned diving bell has been remade into a box the size of a room which is lowered to the bottom and mounted on stilts. It can contain bunks, telephone and television connection with the surface, and presumably other comforts of home. It provides a place for divers working at a depth of a hundred feet or so to rest. Rather than air lines to the surface, the fresh air is provided by tanks of compressed air in the room itself. Since the pressure in the room is equalized with the water pressure outside, the room does not have to be elaborate in structure.

A submersible work-chamber being lowered into the North Sea from the Divcon International oil rig 'Orion'. Cylinders containing oxygen and helium are attached below the spherical chamber.

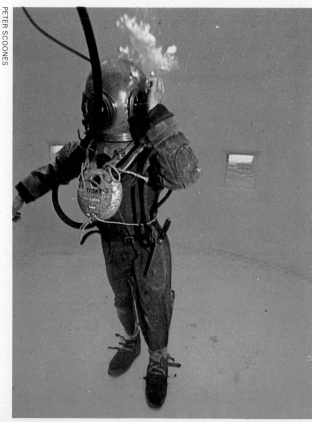

DIVING SUIT

As the technology of diving has been developed over the years, rescue, salvage and repair operations have required diving at great depths and in cold conditions. (Even in warm parts of the world the water gets cold as the diver goes deeper.) The introduction of diving suits has been necessary for protection against *hypothermia* (lowering of the body temperature).

The effects of hypothermia are quite dangerous. As the body temperature is lowered, extremities are affected first. The diver's head is in effect an extremity, and the spinal cord also lies close to the surface of the body. An unclothed diver in water at freezing temperature would be unconscious in minutes. Even at 10 °C (50 °F) his survival time would be little more than $3\frac{1}{2}$ hours, but at this temperature a good diving suit would increase his survival time to around 24 hours by preserving body heat. (Even a garment such as a woollen sweater would reduce the flow of cold water next to the skin and would thus be better than nothing.)

There are two types of diving suits: the helmet suit, which includes the breathing apparatus and completely encloses the diver keeping him warm and dry, and the free-diving or scuba suit, which is independent of the breathing apparatus (AQUA-LUNG). Scuba is an acronym which stands for 'self-contained underwater breathing apparatus'; the scuba suit is so called because it is used in conjunction with the aqualung. Scuba suits are subdivided into two further classifications: the dry suit, which keeps the diver completely dry; and the wet suit, which incorporates a thin film of water between the diver's body and the suit. The water inside the suit is soon warmed by the diver's body and acts as additional insulation against the cold water outside the suit.

The helmet suit The helmet suit was suggested by the earlier DIVING BELL; the helmet itself can be seen as a personal portable diving bell, with the air continually replenished by means of an air line to the surface.

The suit is made of rubberized fabric, and the diver enters it through the neck hole. The helmet is then attached to the suit with a waterproof seal. The helmet has glass ports which enable the diver to see, and is connected to the surface by an air line, through which compressors pump fresh air—supplied at ambient pressure, that is, the pressure of the water surrounding him. Expired air is released via an outlet valve into the water. There is also a secure line for hoisting the diver to the surface and usually a telephone line so that the diver has direct voice contact.

Despite the weight of the helmet suit, the air space within the helmet actually makes the diver positively buoyant. For this reason the suit is equipped with weights to enable the diver to walk on the bottom of the sea. Two weights of approximately 40 lb (18 kg) each are placed one on the chest and the other on the small of the back to maintain equilibrium when walking. In addition the shoes of the suit have soles of lead which weigh about 18 lb (8 kg) apiece. The diver may also wear a belt fitted with lead weights.

The helmet diver can work for long periods underwater because he has a constant supply of air, but because his movement is limited by the lines and the cumbersome heavy suit this type of diving suit is best used for stationary work such as may be involved in working on a wreck.

Above left: an idea for a 'diving machine', about 1803. Left: a more modern design shown in use. The diver in the photo is adjusting his exhaust flow.

Free-diving dry suits These are used in conjunction with foot fins, a mask and the aqualung. A dry suit is a comparatively loose-fitting garment in order to allow for undergarments. It is usually made of rubber or neoprene (an artificial rubber which is more resistant to corrosion), and is sometimes reinforced with fabric. Waterproof seals are provided at the neck and the wrist, and there is a cummerbund-type sealing waist where the top joins the trousers, which have boots attached. (Some dry suits have a neck entry which eliminates the need for the waist seal.)

When the diver is dressed, the undergarments retain some air in them, creating unnecessary buoyancy; the air must be vented off. This can be achieved by inserting one finger under a wrist seal and submerging until only the hands are above water; the water pressure drives the air out. Some suits have a simple duckbill valve which does this automatically.

One of the disadvantages of a dry suit is that as the diver descends the residual quantity of air left in the undergarments is compressed by the water pressure. As the volume of this air decreases, the suit is pressed tighter to the diver, making it rigid and hampering his movement. Sometimes the folds in the suit will trap and pinch the diver's skin, causing welts. For this reason the dry suit is less popular than the wet suit, except in extremely cold water where the warm dry undergarments are a distinct advantage, and in polluted water, where the dry suit is worn in conjunction with a full face mask to protect the

diver from the pollutant. In addition, disinfectant can be poured over the diver before he takes the suit off.

Free-diving wet suits The wet suit consists of a close fitting material, usually foam neoprene, and does not need to be watertight. Water seeps in and is trapped next to the diver's skin, which quickly warms it. Alternatively, warm water may be poured in at the start. The foam material acts as an insulator, containing millions of tiny air bubbles.

The principal disadvantage of the wet suit is that the air bubbles make the diver buoyant, so the aqualung diver is provided with a weighted belt to help him descend. So far so good, as long as the diver is in relatively shallow water, but as the diver descends the ambient pressure reduces the volume of each air bubble. This means a loss of both buoyancy and insulation; the diver who is neutrally buoyant at the surface becomes over-weighted and heavy at depth. (This is one reason why the weighted belt is equipped with a quick-release mechanism.) The experienced diver soon gets used to this change in buoyancy and although it makes ascending more work than descending, the diver can generate quite a lot of power by kicking his feet-fins.

Some methods of avoiding loss of buoyancy have been developed, particularly for commercial divers who spend long periods of time underwater and find the over-weighting exhausting. The most simple is the adjustable buoyancy lifejacket. This is a bag to which is fixed a cylinder of compressed air. As the diver descends he bleeds a little air into the bag to increase his buoyancy. On ascending the air is automatically vented, or discharged manually. A more sophisticated method uses millions of tiny air-filled bubbles of glass, as opposed to the ordinary foam bubbles. The volume of the air in the glass bubbles will not be compressed, so the diver's buoyancy and insulation remain more or less constant. This type of suit, however, is far more expensive.

Below, left and right: two views of a 'deep sea spacesuit'. The suit is designed to withstand pressures of 1000 feet (305 m). The diver breathes air at normal atmospheric pressure; there is a 20 hour supply of oxygen in a back pack. There are four portholes for the diver to see through, and tools can be used by lever-controlled fingers which protrude from the bulbous gloves. The suit is called JIM, stands 6½ feet tall, and is made of magnesium alloy.

DOCKS

For many centuries sea traders relied solely on the shelter afforded by natural harbours, inlets and river estuaries in order to load or discharge, victual or repair their ships. While lying at anchor, their vessels were at the mercy, not only of wind and tide, but of bands of marauders to whom they were easy prey. The need for protection from such threats led to the establishment of basins or wet docks where sailing ships could be fitted out in safety and where their cargoes could be dealt with in relative security.

The word 'dock', which to this day is used fairly loosely to describe a variety of places where ships are berthed, was first used to describe 'an artificial basin filled with water and enclosed by gates' during the second half of the sixteenth century—a period of considerable expansion in maritime trade. One of the first recorded enclosed dock basins was the Howland Great Wet Dock which was built on the south bank of the River Thames in the seventeenth century. Only in the late eighteenth and nineteenth centuries did the great dock-building period begin in earnest, often closely associated with canal and railway-building ventures. This was also the period of the first iron steamships but the tremendous growth in ship sizes since those days has made many early docks obsolete.

The provision of gates at dock entrances is necessary because of the large tidal range which would otherwise cause the basins to have insufficient depth of water at low tide. In many countries the rise and fall of the tide is so insignificant that docks can be completely tidal. For example, in Melbourne, Australia, spring tides (those with the greatest range) rise less than 3 ft (1 m), in Rotterdam about 6.5 ft (2 m); and in Boston, USA, about 10 ft (3 m).

In Britain, however, with its large tidal ranges, more major dock systems are enclosed. The most notable exception to this is at Southampton where all dock berths are tidal, and where the effects of a 13 ft (4 m) tidal range are minimized by a phenomenon known as the 'double tide', which gives six hours of high water a day. An extreme example of a tidal range which makes enclosed docks imperative occurs in the Severn Estuary, where Bristol, for instance, experiences a maximum variation of almost 49 ft (15 m) between high and low water.

Enclosed docks may have a single pair of gates which are open only at high tide when the water levels inside and outside are the same. In order to reduce tidal restrictions on shipping movement, it is more usual to have two or more pairs of gates forming a 'pen' or entrance LOCK, in which ships can be raised or lowered. Such docks are often 'impounded', that is, kept at a high level by powerful pumps drawing water from outside the dock to replace that lost during the locking of ships. Alternatively, water losses can be made good by opening up the lock at high water to refill the dock basin. If the dock walls have been built sufficiently high, there is no reason why the level of water in an impounded dock should not be maintained above the highest level achieved outside, a practice which has long existed in the port of London to give greater depth.

Lock entrances

The dimensions of the lock-pit inevitably govern the maximum size of vessel which can enter an enclosed dock. With the trend towards larger ships in recent years, the constraints of existing entrance locks have become a problem. The largest lock in Britain, at Tilbury, is 1000 ft (305 m) long and 110 ft (33.5 m) wide, with a depth of 45½ ft (14 m), whereas the largest container ships, now operating between Europe and the Far East, are 950 ft (290 m) long overall, 106 ft (32 m) in beam, and have a maximum draught of 42½ ft (12 m). New entrance locks are being built to cater for vessels even larger than this: at the new West Dock at Bristol a lock measuring 1200 ft (366 m) long and 140 ft (43 m) wide is being constructed to take ships of 75,000 tons deadweight, and developments at Le Havre in France include a new lock 1312

Above: the Howland Great Wet Dock near Deptford, later incorporated into the Surrey commercial dock system, was built in the 17th century. Note rows of trees planted as windbreaks.

Right: the Royal group of docks in the Port of London, pictured in October, 1972. A system of locks is necessary because of large tidal ranges.

ft (400 m) in length ar.d 219 ft (67 m) wide, which is claimed to be the world's largest and is capable of accommodating a tanker of 500,000 tons deadweight.

The operation of an entrance lock is basically simple. By using a system of culverts and sluices, water is allowed to pass from the dock into the lock with both inner and outer gates shut. The water level, and with it any ship in the lock, rises until it reaches dock level, when the inner gates open and the ship moves into dock. A departing vessel can then be penned in the lock and lowered by allowing water in the lock to escape through the outer sluices.

Lock gate machinery is usually electrically or hydraulically operated. The gates themselves may each weigh 300 tons or more and are of hollow construction. Different types include gates which are withdrawn into recesses in the lock walls, flap gates which are lowered like a drawbridge to lie flat on the lock bottom, and the more common hinged gates which swing back to open. Large locks often have a third set of gates to form a short lock for handling small vessels more quickly and minimizing water loss. Pairs of gates are invariably angled back slightly in a 'V' against the head of water, so that the water pressure keeps them tightly shut against a sill on the floor.

Dock layouts

Although certain cargoes such as coal or bulk grain require specialized handling facilities, dock berths have traditionally been multipurpose and vary little in design, layout and equipment. Usually the quay apron (the working area alongside ship) is equipped with rail tracks both for CRANES and railway wagons, and is flush-surfaced to give access to road vehicles. Quay cranes of three to five tons capacity at 80 ft (24 m) radius are usually adequate for break-bulk general cargo operations (that is, where individual packages, drums, bales, and so on are handled piecemeal using cargo trays, nets, slings, or hooks), but cranes of greater capacity are installed where heavier cargo, for example steel traffic, is frequently dealt with. For even heavier items many ports are equipped with floating cranes, often with lifting capacities exceeding 100 tons.

Transit sheds adjacent to the quay apron give temporary covered accommodation to cargo prior to its loading aboard ship or collection by road or rail vehicles. Modern sheds have the maximum possible unobstructed floor area so that mobile equipment such as fork lift trucks, platform trucks and mobile cranes can be used to carry and stack cargo. To the rear of the sheds, loading bays with both road and rail access serve for the delivery of goods.

Container docks

The dramatic changes that have occurred in cargo transportation over the past ten years have, however, completely transformed the layout of modern terminals. These new techniques include containerization—the carriage of general goods in large CONTAINERS of internationally standardized dimensions—and 'roll-on roll-off' employing vessels with bow, stern, or side doors through which wheeled freight is loaded and discharged.

A typical container handling dock has a large area of land serving each berth, ideally 20 to 25 acres (8 to 10 hectares), for container marshalling. It does not normally have covered accommodation, except where container stuffing (packing) and unstuffing or Customs examination are carried out, although container warehouses have been constructed with their own internal gantry cranes for stacking.

Two or three giant gantry cranes, with lifting capacities of up to 40 tons, and capable of working a three-minute cycle (that is, loading and unloading 20 containers an hour) may be provided to a berth. For large ocean-going container ships at least 1000 ft (305 m) of quay is allocated for each berth. Mobile handling equipment may include van carriers, which straddle, lift, carry and stack containers three high, tractors and trailers, or side- or front-loaders, each with similar lifting capacities. Alternatively, the gantry cranes may span the entire stacking area, carrying out all movements between ship, container stack,

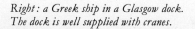

Above: minesweepers in dry dock in Brest, France. The ships are supported and the water pumped out of the dock. The ships must be carefully positioned on the structure. Dry docks are necessary for repair of the rudder and other parts below water line.

Right: a Greek ship in a Glasgow dock. The dock is well supplied with cranes.

and inland transport.

With large container ships carrying 2000 or more containers and perhaps discharging half of these at one port and then loading a similar number, the operation of a container terminal is highly complex. For this reason computer control of container movements is widely used, and studies are already in hand with a view to the automation of future container berths, perhaps with fleets of 'robotugs' responding to radio signals.

Ferry terminals

Although many roll-on roll-off ferry terminals cater for passengers as well as freight and have passenger facilities of varying degrees of refinement, roll-on roll-off terminals consist mainly of a ramp, shore bridge, or linkspan on to which the ferry can open its doors, and a large marshalling area for the vehicles it carries. In some cases a simple concrete ramp built out from the quay wall is all that is necessary, but most shore bridges are tailor-made for the individual vessel using them, with electrically operated machinery able to compensate for the ferry's changing draught during loading operations. Like all very successful ideas roll-on roll-off is a simple concept and it has revolutionized the carriage of cargo on short sea routes.

Bulk terminals

The economics of transportation are resulting in the building of increasingly large vessels for BULK HANDLING of raw materials but arrangements must be made to accommodate them. *Globtik Tokyo* and *Globtik London*, the largest tankers afloat, are 477,000 tons deadweight, 1243 ft (382 m) long, and have a draught of 92 ft 6 in (28 m). Oil tankers are usually brought to jetties sited in deep water but a relatively new system of loading and unloading uses what is known as a single point mooring buoy or monobuoy mooring, linked by pipeline to the shore installations, and which is placed as far out to sea as is necessary.

Special dock facilities exist for other bulk traffics, iron ore being a prime example. Vessels of 100,000 tons or more are now regularly employed carrying ore to Europe from Australia, Brazil and Canada. Modern terminals such as the British Transport Docks Board's Port Talbot Harbour in South Wales work around the clock 365 days of the year when necessary; their transporter cranes fitted with 20-ton capacity grabs are capable of average discharge rates of 1800 tons an hour.

Dry docks and floating docks

At regular intervals all ships need to be inspected 'in the dry', and sometimes repaired. For this reason, most major ports are equipped with dry, or graving, docks; slipways being used for smaller ships.

Dry docks, which usually take one ship at a time, are simply basins which are capable of being pumped dry to leave a ship supported by an arrangement of 'keel blocks', so that work can be carried out on the hull, propellers, or rudder. The procedure for drydocking a ship is a precise affair and may take several hours; with the dock flooded the gate is opened and the ship enters, then the gate is closed and pumping begins. Accurate positioning is vital as the ship settles on to the blocks, prearranged to fit her hull, and to facilitate this, modern dry docks are usually fitted with guidance systems. In many international ports dry docks are being provided for the largest tankers afloat or planned: the port of Rotterdam already has a dry dock 1350 ft (412 m) long, which can accommodate 500,000-ton tankers, and the construction of a super dry dock for 700,000-tonners will be carried out at Kiel over the next two years.

The purpose of a floating dock is the same as that of a conventional dry dock, only the method of getting the ship out of the water differs. Ballast tanks are used to raise the submerged dock towards the surface and with it the ship to be repaired.

A large floating dock would have a lifting capacity of 20,000 tons, which would enable it to deal with ships of up to 70,000 tons deadweight. Such a dock, ordered recently for the Scandinavian port of Aalborg, will be 750 ft (228 m) long, 120 ft (37 m) wide between the inner walls and 148 ft (45 m) wide.

DOLBY TECHNIQUE (see tape recorder)

Left: another type of dry dock, the floating dry dock. This one is in Hamburg. The ship is raised out of the water by ballast tanks in the submerged dock. Such a dock can lift ships of 70,000 tons deadweight.

Above: the King George V dock of the London Port Authority. Henry VIII started the first Royal docks in 1509. Today HM docks are controlled by a director general, a naval officer.

marshalling area

unloading

container terminal: sealed
units are unloaded directly
or stored in marshalling a

dock enclosure (fixed water level)

lock gates for
use with small
ships to save water

roll-on roll-off ferry
for private vehicles

passenger terminals
and customs sheds

main lock gates retain water in dock
at higher level than outside

lighter-aboard-ship (LASH) syst
allows large ships to moor in tida
while tugs remove the lighters

open tidal water

dry dock for repair work

goods unloading

goods collection area
for road transport

iner
rains

transit sheds

rail access

road access

floating dock

JANECLARE

CHAELJOHN

B.H

DOOR CLOSER

The simplest type of door closer is a spring, but a spring closes the door as fast as it can, which results in a slam. A pneumatic or hydraulic door closer combines a spring with a piston, so that the spring closes the door and the piston acts as a shock absorber, controlling the rate of movement of the door, and sometimes providing a 'latching' pressure against the internal spring of a Yale type lock.

In climates which are quite cold in the winter and very hot in the summer, a house will have a storm door on the outside of the door frame. The storm door is a light door with interchangeable panels: a pane of glass for the winter months and a screen for the summer, to admit breezes but keep out insects. Such a light door will usually have an inexpensive pneumatic door closer, resembling a bicycle pump and comprising a tube made of aluminium containing a spring and a simple air cylinder. The spring closes the door and the air pressure inside the tube slowly escapes, softening the slam. One end of the device has a hinged bracket on it and the other end is the end of the piston rod, with a smaller bracket attached. The device is mounted between the door and the door frame.

For heavier doors which are opened and closed all day long, for example the front door of a shop, the automatic door closer is somewhat more elaborate, using a *hydraulic* cylinder (filled with fluid, in this case oil). The hydraulic door closer can be oblong in shape if it uses an ordinary coil spring, or 'pot' shaped if it uses a clock type spiral spring. In either case the device contains a rack and pinion gear system.

The closer is mounted on the door, and the pinion spindle, which projects from the body, is connected to the door frame by an arm. When the door is opened this arm turns the spindle

Above left: a concealed type of door closer which is fitted into the floor and covered by a flush-fitting metal plate, cut away in this picture to show the spring mechanism. This type is used for swinging doors which open in both directions.

Above right: a fully adjustable door closer consisting of a spring cylinder fitted into the inner edge of the door, and an anchor plate which is secured to the door jamb. It can be used on standard single and double internal doors of up to 112 lb (51 kg) weight, and can operate through any angle up to 180°.

Below: an automatic door closer. As the door is opened the pinion rotates on its spindle along the rack, pushing the piston back against the hydraulic pressure of the oil and compressing the spring. As the door is released the piston returns along the rack and oil leaks slowly through a one-way valve to the front compartment.

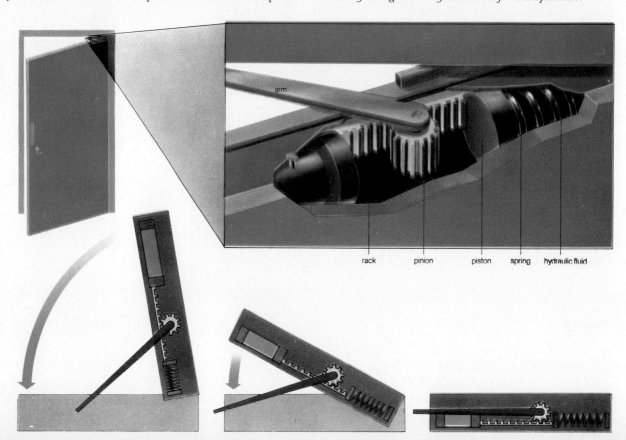

arm

rack   pinion   piston   spring   hydraulic fluid

which rotates the pinion against the rack on the piston body driving it back against the spring pressure. In the pot-shaped door closer, the turning of the pinion winds up the spring; in the oblong design the spring is located inside the cylinder behind the piston.

Driving the piston back forces the oil out through a one-way valve to the front of the casing. When the door is released it is closed by the action of the spring which attempts to force the piston back along the bore, turning the spindle, consequently closing the door. The rate of door closure is controlled by a needle valve which slowly admits the oil back into the cylinder. The needle valve, hence door movement, is adjustable. By unscrewing the regulating screw the oil flows more freely and the door can be closed fairly quickly. One reason for making the device adjustable is because in cold weather the oil becomes thick and sluggish, although silicon-based and high-quality lubricating oils are available whose viscosity remains more or less constant. Some closers are adjustable between three seconds and 120 seconds of door closing time.

The latching function, if required, is supplied by short-circuiting the oil flow at the very end of the piston movement by means of a second needle valve. When the oil pressure is gone, the spring takes over and provides a final push to latch the door.

The hydraulic door closers described are the most commonly used but there are many additional types to suit particular applications. These include units which hold-open for pre-scribed periods, totally concealed closers which leave the lines of the door unmarred, and hold-open types which have electronic heat sensors built in and which close the door automatically in the event of fire.

DOPPLER EFFECT

With any wave-type motion the apparent frequency—the pitch of a sound or the colour of a light—is determined by the rate at which the waves pass the observer. If there is relative motion between the source and observer the apparent frequency will be altered, the frequency of wave-encounters being raised if the source and observer are moving towards each other and lowered if they are moving apart.

The effect, first investigated by Austrian physicist C J Doppler in 1842, is often evident when a moving source of sound, such as an aircraft, racing car or train (especially a train sounding a whistle or hooter) passes close to the observer. The noise approaches as a high-pitched note and swiftly falls to a much lower pitch, passing through the true pitch for the source at the point where source and observer are closest together and have instantaneously no relative motion along the line joining them.

There are few applications of the Doppler effect with sound and similar vibrations involving matter, but in the case of ELECTROMAGNETIC RADIATION it has already been put to many uses. In 1848 Fizeau verified the validity of the concept with light, and soon astronomers began to study the spectra of stars (see SPECTROSCOPY) and discovered an apparent shift of wave-length or frequency in many of them, interpreted as indicative of motion relative to the Earth. This Doppler shift has been

Below: the Doppler effect. A wave is emitted simultaneously in all directions but by the time the next wave front is released the aeroplane has moved forward, with the result the waves are compressed in front, giving a higher pitch, and attenuated to the rear for a lower pitch. A similar effect is experienced with light waves from stars.

DIAGRAM VISUAL INFORMATION LTD

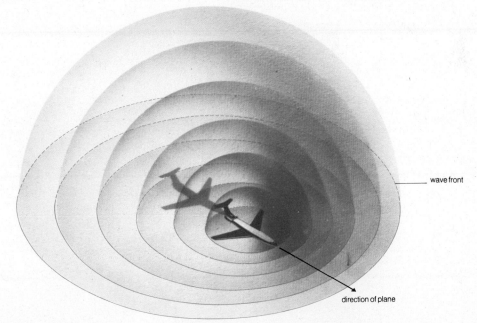

wave front

direction of plane

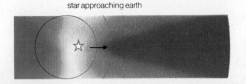

star approaching earth

observer (earth)

star travelling away from earth

used to calculate stellar velocities and, in the case of orbital bodies such as binary stars, planets and planetary moons, their orbits and distances.

In the present century it was realized that the shift of what appear to be the most distant objects is towards the red end of the spectrum, this lengthening of the apparent wavelength signifying motion away from the solar system. By 1940 the *red shift* was accepted as strongly indicative of an expanding Universe, with the most distant visible objects receding at the highest speeds.

In the field of RADAR, Doppler effects have become enormously important. By 1950 military radars were beginning to incorporate MTI (moving target indication) by adding circuits which instantly detect reflected signals subject to a Doppler shift while ignoring reflections from fixed targets. Thus the radar could at once spot an aircraft approaching low down in front of a distant hillside. Today Doppler radars are so sensitive they can be used as BURGLAR ALARMS. A miniature aerial can 'illuminate' a courtyard or other space and signal the alarm if an intruder were to creep in at the slowest practical rate of human motion. Other Doppler radars are carried by aircraft as navigation aids, to measure relative motion between aircraft and ground (see AVIONICS) with special corrections being applied for wave motion when flying over the ocean. This principle is also used in radar speed checks on cars.

Evidence for an expanding universe. On the left are galaxies—huge star systems—each progressively smaller and fainter. On the right are their spectra, the long streaks between pairs of reference spectra produced at the telescope. The more distant the galaxy, the more the distinctive 'H' and 'K' lines, due to ionized calcium, are shifted to the red end as indicated by the arrow. The actual distances to the galaxies must be found separately, for example by detecting stars of known brightness in them.

cluster nebula	distance in light-yrs	red-shifts
		H+K
Virgo	78,000,000	1,200 Km/sec
Ursa Major	1,000,000,000	15,000 Km/sec
Corona Borealis	1,400,000,000	22,000 Km/sec
Bootes	2,500,000,000	39,000 Km/sec
Hydra	3,960,000,000	61,000 Km/sec

HALE OBSERVATORIES

DOWSING

Dowsing, also known popularly as water divining, is a method of finding things, generally underground, by the use of a natural sensitivity in man which is neither properly understood nor explicable in conventional scientific terms. The sensitivity is present in most people to a greater or lesser degree, but is not known to be connected with any physical part of the brain or sensory apparatus. Nevertheless, it incontestably exists; dowsing is a practical method of finding water and, though this is less well known universally, certain other things as well.

Dowsing has been practised for at least 2000 years. It is thought that the ability has always been present in man, but has atrophied through the years as the need for it became less with the growth of civilization. In recent centuries it has been discouraged by religious authorities.

Applications The applications of dowsing today are varied and include the location of water, minerals, oil, archaeological sites, and cables, pipes or drains. Furthermore it is also possible to estimate the depth of the object below the surface. Other applications of dowsing include finding missing people or lost articles, the diagnosis and treatment of illness and soil analysis. All aspects of dowsing, however, are serious practical fields of dowsing and are not for the inexperienced. To be proficient and reliable the dowser must know the background of the field in which he is working and be experienced, as a dowser, in that field.

Tools and methods Because dowsing is a highly individualistic art, the tools and methods used vary a great deal. Often a dowser will know the answer through his sensitivity

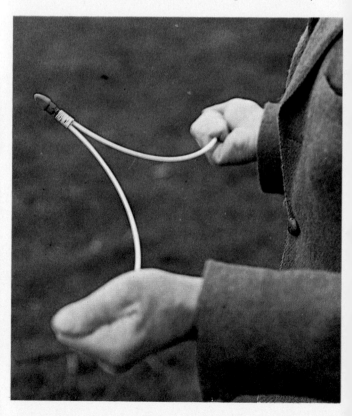

These photographs show one dowser's code of rod movement. There are, however, many others. Here the V rod is held in a position of tension, in the search position at the start of a walk.

but it is better conveyed to him by some vital indication, so tools are used. These are moved by the dowser's muscles, even if subconsciously, the movement corresponding to the individual's own adopted code of signals.

Three main groups of tools are used: angle rods, pendulums and hands. The actual size and weight of the angle rod or pendulum is left to the preference of the dowser. Angle rods are often pieces of fence wire bent at right angles. The hand-held part is usually about 8 inch (20 cm) and the other part about 18 inch (46 cm). Rods are held loosely in the hand with the long arm pointing forward. Pendulums may be any size and made of any material. Small ones are often used indoors by skilled operators in conjunction with maps, while the larger ones are sometimes preferred for outdoor work. Some dowsers may use their hands alone for outdoor work.

The modern dowser often works in three stages: firstly at home using a map or plan, secondly at the location itself to confirm or if necessary correct the findings made at home, and lastly by carrying out a test dig, or whatever is the appropriate proof action.

Many people who have the sensitivity to be good dowsers do not know that they possess it, and would not believe it if told. This attitude in itself prevents successful use of the technique, and so, on the other hand, do preconceived ideas and wishful thinking. The sensitivity must be carefully developed (rather than gained where it never existed before) by practice on simple tasks with demonstrable results, keeping questions in the mind regarding what is sought absolutely clear and appropriate.

PHOTOS: JULIETTE MUSKETT

Angle rods are frequently used by dowsers. In the search position they are held loosely in the hand with the long arm pointing forward (top). On approaching the object, the muscles move the rods inward until they are in the 'found' position (bottom).

As the dowser walks over the area undergoing investigation, on approaching the object sought, his arm muscles start moving the rod, until over the object it is in the 'found' position.

DRAGSTER

A dragster is a specialized type of racing car which competes against a clock, or against another car on a parallel track, in a *drag race*. A drag race is essentially an acceleration test on a quarter-mile (400 m) track called a *drag strip*.

Stock car racing, that is, racing of modified production cars, is said to have developed during the Prohibition era in the United States (1919–33). Bootleggers of illegal spirits tuned up and modified the engines of their cars so they could outrun the police. Since World War II drag racing, an outgrowth of racing of modified cars by amateurs, has become a very popular spectator sport. A dragster starting from a standstill can cover the quarter-mile in as little as 6.5 seconds, reaching a speed of 200 miles an hour and requiring a parachute to help stop it.

The engine American V-8 engines are popular for use in dragsters because of the high capacity, expressed in cubic inches, of their fuel combustion chambers. (See INTERNAL COMBUSTION ENGINE.) Ordinary automobile engines are built for durability and a certain minimum fuel consumption, factors which do not concern the drag racer, so the engines are completely disassembled and put back together with a great deal of balancing and polishing of the parts. The object is to make the engine lighter and capable of achieving the maximum revolutions per minute in the shortest possible time. The cooling system—radiator, hoses and water pump—is dispensed with, since the water in the engine's water jacket is sufficient for cooling during the quarter-mile run. (Dispensing with the water pump also restores power to the engine which is normally used in operating the pump by means of a belt off the crankshaft.) The rebuilt engine incorporates a SUPERCHARGER and a FUEL INJECTION SYSTEM; the fuel itself may be a nitro-methanol mixture which is highly combustible. The exhaust system consists of tuned pipes of exactly the right diameter to match the manifold on the engine for the right amount of back-pressure. Silencers [mufflers] are dispensed with, making drag strips very noisy places.

The chassis For a certain class of drag racing, a slightly modified engine may be mounted in an ordinary car body, but a true dragster is a glamorous construction completely unsuitable for driving on the street. It may be built from scratch of welded steel tubing, with an aluminium 'skin' covering it, and providing barely enough space for the driver. The tremendous accelerating power of a dragster tends to make the front end want to climb into the air, so it may be made as long as 30 ft, and the snout will be aerodynamically designed to keep it on the ground. The so-called 'slingshot' dragster has the frame extending well beyond the rear axle, and the driver's seat is located there, like the stone in a slingshot.

The rear axle halves themselves are often shortened to lessen the risk of snapping with the torque of acceleration. The wheels are 'mag' wheels made of magnesium alloy, combining light weight with high strength. 'Wrinkle-wall' tyres without any treads are used for maximum traction (the drag strip must be absolutely dry and clean). This type of tyre is called a *slick* and is able to distort under acceleration without deflating. The mechanics sometimes pour bleach over the tyres just before take-off to make them grip better.

Drag racing, originally the province of amateurs, has become so costly that the dragsters are nowadays often sponsored by garages, auto supply shops and similar businesses.

Left: last-minute adjustments are made to a dragster just before the race. The manifold pipes are specially made and tuned to provide the correct back pressure, allowing the engine to produce as much power as possible.

Below: a 'slingshot' dragster on the drag strip. Car racing was already an established sport as early as 1895; drag racing is the most specialized, being a simple acceleration test. Drag racing is closely policed by the National Hot Rod Association in the USA, to overcome bad publicity caused by illegal street racing.

DRAINAGE

Drainage is the removal or control of surplus surface water, subsoil water or sewage. The main types of drainage are land drainage and town drainage, which includes sewage disposal.

In its natural state the earth can control its own drainage fairly well. Vegetational cover takes the initial impact from rain and protects the topsoil, whose humus (decomposed organic matter) content can absorb water and whose structure assists the percolation of the remaining water. The surplus flows into small streams which in turn produce a system of rivers, whose size steadily increases towards the sea.

Soils, however, vary greatly in the main single factor which affects their natural drainage, *permeability* (for example, gravelly soils may be 50,000 times more permeable than clay). (The permeability of soil is the rate at which water can seep through it.) In addition, higher lands usually have steeper slopes and more permeable soils than lower lands, and thus have better natural drainage. Man's usage of land, however, has tended to

Right: deepening the sewer in Fleet Street, London, in 1845.

Below: one of the most extensive urban drainage systems in ancient Asia was at Mohenjo-Daro in the Indus valley, around 2000 BC.

Below: land drainage. Some of the earliest forms of drainage consisted of systems of open channels or ditches forming networks across the fields, finally converging on a main ditch or river. Clay tiles or jointed cylindrical clay pipes are used for underground drainage. Water enters the pipes from the surrounding gravel at the joints and flows away to the outfall.

RADIO TIMES HULTON PICTURE LIBRARY

MACQUITTY COLLECTION

mole plough

open channel drains

underground drains

'mole' drainage

DIAGRAM VISUAL INFORMATION LTD

impair natural drainage. Soils comprise about half solid particles, and half pore space which is filled with air and water. Without drainage the pore space can become waterlogged. The uppermost surface of the waterlogged zone is called the *water table*; in good land the water table is deeper than 6 ft (1.8 m) from the soil surface.

The main objects of land drainage, LAND RECLAMATION, EROSION CONTROL, FLOOD CONTROL, and prevention of water-logging, are achieved by lowering the water table—that is, by removing the water from the soil or subsoil at a faster rate than it can accumulate.

There are indications that the Chinese used drainage systems for land restoration as long ago as 2300 BC. Since then localized independent efforts at drainage improvement have progressed to co-ordinated measures for control of surplus water through-out whole areas. In these land areas, known as catchment areas, all the water drains into reservoirs, lakes, or river systems.

Land drainage

The four main land-drainage methods are: open channel drains, underground pipes, 'mole' drainage, and pumping. In open channel drains or ditches gravity pro-vides the force that removes excess water. They vary in size from small ditches, dug by hand or hydraulic excavators or trenchers and often seen around the perimeters of fields, to large channels 15 ft (4.6 m) or more deep, constructed by powered dragline excavators. The channels eventually feed into a river system, lake or reservoir.

Underground pipes were developed from 'covered tiles', first used in England in the late eighteenth century and made by bending an ordinary clay tile to an inverted 'U' cross-section before baking it and laying it on a flat tile to produce a channel. By the mid-nineteenth century extruded cylindrical pipes were produced by machinery, and concrete pipes appeared a little later. The pipes, which are 2 ft (61 cm) in length, have spigot joints (one end of the pipe is larger than the other, and the small end of one pipe fits into the large end of the next) which allow some flexibility to cater for ground subsidence. The pipes are placed in temporary trenches about 2 ft (61 cm) wide by 3 to 6 ft (0.9 to 1.8 m) deep, generally made by trenching machines which are either self-powered or drawn by large tractors. Gravel or permeable filler is then placed on top of the pipes and finally the topsoil is replaced. Water flows into the pipes at the joints, which are protected by finely screened gravel, or tarred paper to resist any inflow of silt, which could cause a blockage. The pipes are usually arranged in parallel runs, known as main drains, fed at right angles by lateral runs. Spacing between the pipes is influenced by the permeability of the soil. The main drains are laid on a gradient and eventually feed through an *outfall* into a river system or reservoir.

Plastic pipes have recently been introduced, which can be wound into large coils and then laid by a suitably adapted trenching machine.

Mole drainage consists of moulding drainage channels into the subsoil without any artificial lining. The system requires a stone-free clay soil and an even slope. Channels, parallel to the ground surface, about 2 ft (61 cm) deep, 6 inch (15 cm) in di-ameter and 3 to 5 yd (2.7 to 4.6 m) apart, are made by a mole

Below: domestic drainage, illustrating the separate system in which foul drainage and surface water are collected separately. Sewage and general waste from the house itself passes into one of the main pipes and flows away to be treated at the sewage disposal works. Another system of pipes receives the rain and surface water.

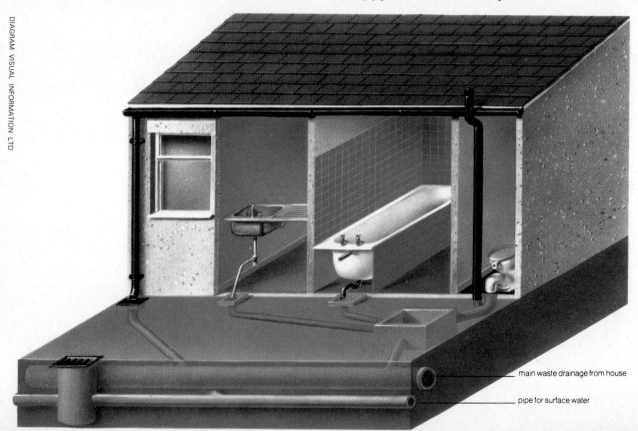

main waste drainage from house

pipe for surface water

plough. This has a vertical knife blade carrying a horizontal bullet-shaped bottom member, was invented in about 1800 and is the forerunner of a machine now capable of fabricating concrete drain pipes in the mole channel, thus avoiding the need for digging and refilling trenches. The modern practice is to use mole channels in combination with pipe systems, the channels running at right angles to the pipes and feeding into the permeable material on top of the pipes.

Pumping water from below the water table is carried out in areas where the water level is so low, perhaps below sea level, that gravity drainage is not possible. The most common arrangement is for a pumping station to receive water from a low lying area and pump it to an embanked river and hence to the sea.

Town drainage
In towns, drains are needed for both sewage and for the surface water that is collected from the many impermeable surfaces such as roads and roofs.

There are three principal methods of town drainage. In the 'combined system' a single main sewer under the street carries all the sewage and all the surplus surface water to a sewage disposal unit (see SEWAGE TREATMENT). With this system it would be expensive to have main sewers large enough to carry all the rainfall which might occur in a heavy storm, and it would tax sewage disposal units to handle such large volumes. Therefore it is usual to provide storm water overflows which discharge directly into rivers when the water level in the main sewer is too high. As the amount of sewage relative to the amount of rainwater is very low in these circumstances, pollution is not usually a problem, and the large volumes of rainwater have a cleansing action on the system. This system is simple and cheap, and is often used in rural areas where the amount of sewage is not high, and in coastal towns where untreated sewage is piped out to sea to be carried away by tidal action.

An alternative drainage method is the 'separate system' in which a main sewer under the street carries all the domestic sewage and industrial effluents to a sewage disposal unit, and a main drain carries all the surplus surface water into a river, lake or reservoir. This method has largely been superseded by the 'partially separate system' in which a main sewer under the street carries all the drainage from buildings (both sewage and the surface water from roofs) and a main drain carries all the surface water from the roads. Whichever system is used, rain-

HOWARD ROTAVATORS

BRISTOL CORPORATION/PHOTO · J PORTER

Top: a trench digging machine adapted for laying plastic pipe. This machine can also be used for laying unjoined cylindrical clay pipes, which are fed into the layer by hand as the machine moves forward.

Centre: a cutting machine used in digging storm water tunnels. The rotating head cuts into the tunnel face, and the material removed is collected by the circular conveyer at the front which passes it to the rear of the machine, where it is taken away by rail trucks. The machine itself is self-propelled and runs on crawler tracks.

Bottom: the entrance to a twin-tunnel storm water drainage system in Bristol, England, part of a scheme to prevent flooding in low-lying areas of the city south of the River Avon.

water from roofs is collected in a similar way. Rainwater is drained into a gutter around the roof perimeter by the slope of the roof, and is discharged through vertical downpipes into the drain system. Roads are built with a camber to drain surface water into roadside gutters. The surface water is then discharged at intervals through gullies into the drain system. On rural roads surface water is often led straight into open roadside ditches, or into 'French drains', which are trenches filled with pebbles or large stones through which the water can easily percolate. Embankments are often drained by French drains.

Drains vary in diameter from 4 inch (10 cm) for household purposes to several yards for main sewers, according to the amount of flow they are expected to carry. Small drains are usually constructed from iron or stoneware pipe and as size increases precast concrete is used. Trenching methods similar to those for land drainage are used but concrete foundations are usually provided to resist damage to the pipes by ground settlement. Also the pipe joints are made watertight by sealing the spigot with cement or bituminous compounds. If drains or sewers are particularly large or deep, tunnelling methods may be used. Drains are laid on a gradient to provide the required flow to the point of discharge. For maintenance purposes covered inspection chambers known as 'manholes' are fitted at regular intervals, providing access from the road surface into the drain.

Below: concreting the floor of a drainage tunnel. The shallow channel running along the tunnel floor will carry the normal flow, but after a heavy storm there may be enough water to fill the whole tunnel.

BRISTOL CORPORATION/PHOTO: J PORTER

DRAWING of metals

Drawing is a term which may be applied to two main groups of processes, typified by *wire-drawing* and *deep drawing*. Metal products which are deep drawn include cartridge casings for bullets, shallow tins for food such as sardines, and the DWI beverage can (see CAN MANUFACTURE).

Wire, bar and tube drawing These processes reduce the cross-sectional area of a length of metal by pulling it through a hole in a die or drawplate which is smaller than the material entering it. This method of reduction has been known since pre-Christian times, and with the use of modern techniques is capable of producing almost all metals and alloys in the form of wire.

The process usually starts with hot rolled or extruded rod or bar. This must be prepared by treatment with suitable chemicals such as dilute sulphuric acid to render its surface free of oxide, scale or other unwanted impurities. Steel may be coated with zinc phosphate to provide a suitable base for lubrication, and hard metals that are difficult to draw may be coated with softer metals to facilitate the process. The workpiece is then reduced in stages by passing it through a series of dies, each having an orifice smaller than the previous one, until the required size is attained. The greater the reduction imposed in a given pass the larger is the required drawing force. The permissible reduction in each pass is therefore limited by the strength of the emergent wire and does not often exceed 30%. Thus, a great many passes and dies are required to produce fine wire. For continuous operation lengths of rod are welded together before drawing.

Although early dies were made of tool steel, it is now usual to employ inserts of sintered tungsten carbide or diamond, the latter being employed for the finer gauges of diameter 1 mm or less. The design of the die is very important: the simplest practicable arrangement consists of a conical entry leading to a *land* which preserves accuracy of size, but more complex forms may be employed. These influence the magnitude of the draw-

Below: hot drawing in a wire rod and baling factory in West Pakistan.

Below right: the drawn steel wire exits from the die box to be wound onto the 'block'. The die box contains a tungsten carbide die; the lubricant used is an industrial soap powder. The machine operator checks the size of the wire with a micrometer.

COLORIFIC/PHOTO: P BOUCAS

ing load and also the uniformity of deformation within the wire.

It is always necessary to provide lubrication. Thick bars may be drawn dry, using soap powders, but wires are commonly drawn wet with liberal application of soluble oils or soap solutions. The operating parts of multi-die drawing machines, used for the production of very fine wires, may be immersed in a bath of lubricant.

As the drawing process proceeds the workpiece hardens and becomes more resistant to further deformation. It may be necessary to *anneal* the wire to restore its ductility. (Annealing is a mild HEAT TREATMENT.)

Drawing is important in the production of tubes and seamless pipe, and three main methods are used: sinking, plug drawing and mandrel drawing. In sinking, the tube is drawn hollow, allowing the tube wall to thicken somewhat. The other two methods permit the wall thickness to be controlled by having inside the tube either a plug, which stays in position within the die, or a mandrel, which passes through the die with the tube. It is possible to produce very fine tubes for medical and other purposes, such as the inoculation of flies for research into tropical diseases, or the insemination of queen bees. The smallest tube produced so far was made in Britain and has an outside diameter of 13 microns (0.000515 inch) and a bore of 3.3 microns (0.00013 inch).

Deep drawing Deep drawing is a method of shaping sheet in which a flat sheet of metal is squeezed between a male punch and a female die so as to assume a deep hollow shape. (The term should not be applied to the production of shallow forms, such as domestic radiators and automobile door panels, which are more properly described as pressings.) As the punch progressively penetrates the die, taking the blank with it, the undrawn part of the blank must be prevented from wrinkling, usually by applying a load to the edges. The whole operation makes very severe demands on the material being drawn, and metallic materials differ widely in their suitability for this type of working. Sheet intended for deep drawing must be processed by special methods to improve its capacity for deep drawing, but with any given type of material there is a limit to what can be achieved in this respect, and much depends upon skill and experience in the design of tools and operational methods. Deep drawing materials are usually soft and ductile with only small amounts of alloying elements.

DREDGER

Dredgers, also called dredges, are floating excavation machines used for keeping harbours, canals and navigable waterways free from excessive accumulations of mud and silt. In modern times several other functions of dredgers have developed, including supplying material for land reclamation, collecting gravel and sand for the construction industry, and mining diamonds, gold, tin and other minerals from the inshore sea bed.

Centuries ago dredging was carried out by the 'bag and spoon' method, using manual labour. The forerunners of modern dredgers were developed in the middle of the seventeenth century, and were powered by horses until the advent of the steam engine. By 1900 dredgers of the bucket, grab and dipper type were in use. In the present century the power source is usually a DIESEL ENGINE, connected directly to the machinery or operating a generator which produces electricity (see DYNAMO).

The twentieth century has seen two important developments in dredging technology. Firstly, with the aid of SURVEYING techniques and modern electronic NAVIGATION aids, dredging has become a more precise operation where necessary; secondly,

Below : two types of dredgers. The drawing is an illustration from a 19th century encyclopedia showing a steam-powered chain and bucket dredger, not much different in principle from those still in use today. The chain is driven by means of a pinion and ring gear, and the ladder is lowered by a crane. The photograph shows a modern suction dredger working in the Panama canal.

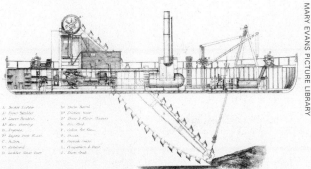

the efficient suction method of dredging is rendering older types of dredgers obsolescent, except for very small operations where very hard materials have to be removed.

Bucket dredgers

The bucket dredger was for many years the most common type, and many such machines are still in use today. It is essentially a chain-and-bucket CONVEYER, strung on a frame called a *ladder*, which is hydraulically raised and lowered at the appropriate angle to the bottom. The bucket dredger is usually not self-propelled, and must be towed to the site by a tugboat. It is used in conjunction with hopper barges, which haul the dredged material out to sea to dump it. The bucket dredger is secured with anchors, and can be manœuvred over its working area to a limited extent by pulling in one anchor cable and letting out another. The most serious disadvantage of the bucket dredger is that when it is used in shipping channels it tends to be in the way of commerce.

Grab and dipper dredgers

The dipper is a mechanical shovel which pivots on a boom, and the grab is the familiar 'clamshell', or pair of hinged jaws for grabbing bulk materials, suspended by cables from the end of a boom. Grab dredgers and dipper dredgers are more manœuvrable than bucket dredgers, and can work in awkward corners and close to quay walls. Some of them are self-propelled and have their own hoppers, so that they can haul their own spoil to the

Above: a grab dredger in a yacht haven. Basically a floating diesel powered crane with a cable operated grab, it is mounted in an unpowered barge and can operate in a confined space.

Below: a stationary bucket dredger. This can excavate areas of the bank just above the water line as long as the bottom tumbler shaft remains immersed to prevent overheating.

ALLARD GRAPHIC ARTS

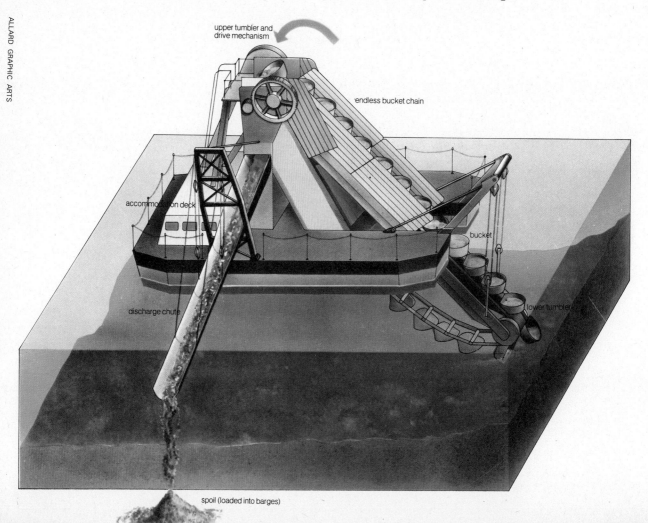

upper tumbler and drive mechanism

endless bucket chain

accommodation deck

bucket

discharge chute

lower tumbler

spoil (loaded into barges)

dumping ground. During the dredging part of their operation, they are usually secured by lines fore and aft; it is the deck winches and the derricking of the boom which provide the manœuvrability. They are usually fitted with *spuds*—extendable legs which reach to the bottom—to provide stability and leverage against the material being dredged.

Suction dredgers There are several types of suction dredger, all making use of the centrifugal pump. The impeller of such a pump causes suction by its spinning action which pulls water and solids up from the bottom through an airtight tube. The discharge of the tube is directed into the centre of the spining impeller, and the discharge vent of the pump is around the outside of the casing. Some dredgers have several pumps going at once. The tube can be made flexible with airtight fittings at the joints.

Where the material to be dredged is soft and granular, such as sand or gravel, no further refinements are needed, but for other applications the suction device has been adapted for use with cutters, drag-arms and scrapers ('dustpans') to loosen the material or break it up. The sucking end of the suction tube is located near the mechanical device in order to collect the spoil as it is broken up.

The suction drag-arm vessel has a conventional sea-going hull, and the drag-arm is mounted underneath it. The hoppers

Below: a suction dredger. This type of dredger can be used for the removal of fairly loose sand or gravel but is limited by the size of particle which will pass through the pump. High pressure jets around the suction head erode the sides of the bank under the water line. The hull is moved along by winch lines attached to the shore or to anchors on the bottom digging a series of overlapping pits. The spoil is piped into barges or directly ashore.

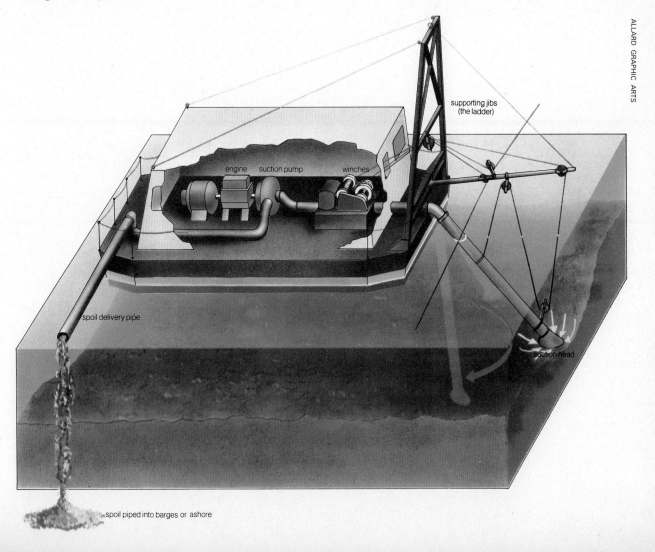

supporting jibs
(the ladder)

engine   suction pump   winches

spoil delivery pipe

suction head

spoil piped into barges or ashore

KEYSTONE PRESS AGENCY LTD

for the spoil are built into the hull as well. The cutterhead dredger has a revolving cutter at the end of a ladder; the cutter chops impacted material out of the bottom so that the suction device can handle it.

Some suction dredgers have spuds for stability in relatively shallow water; some have floating pipelines which can be extended some distance from the ship for dumping the spoil as soon as it is sucked up. Suction dredgers can be fitted with chutes in such a way that they deliver the spoil to waiting barges or dockside dump trucks. A suction dredger used in a land reclamation project can suck the spoil from the bottom and 'shoot' the solids straight over a nearby embankment into the area being filled in.

Water picked up along with the solids by the suction operation is allowed to spill out by means of overflow troughs, the solid material settling to the bottom of the trough or hopper.

The largest modern dredgers have hopper capacities of around 12,000 tons, and capacities up to 30,000 tons are expected soon. Larger dredging operations are being made necessary by the large size of modern super-tankers, which require large-scale excavation of dock-side waters at oil terminals.

Above: a tin dredger 394 feet (120 m) long and weighing 2800 tons. The ladder is raised and lowered into the material to be dredged by means of the cables.

Below: a chain and bucket dredger of the type used to remove silt from canal and river bottoms. The dredger can be manoeuvred to a limited extent by manipulating the anchor chains.

HART ASSOCIATES

DRILL, dental

The dental drill is an instrument used in DENTISTRY for the deep penetration of tooth structure. It is used to remove infected and softened parts of decayed tooth substance (dental caries) and also to shape and prepare the remaining sound tooth to receive the filling or restoration. Rotary instruments are also used to cut, grind and polish in many other dental procedures.

History

Originally, cavities in the teeth were prepared with hand instruments such as tiny spoon-shaped excavators, chisels and files. Some of the files were rounded and were used by rotating their pencil-shaped handles between the operator's thumb and fingers while the instrument was steadied in the palm of the hand. T-shaped crutch handles and finger-rings with cups on them were also employed to give the operator greater control of the file. Interchangeable file-tips or burs could be attached to the handles as they became blunted with use. One immediate disadvantage of these straight drills was that the operating tip could not be carried into some of the more inaccessible places at the back of the mouth.

By the middle of the nineteenth century a two-handled Merry's drill-stock was introduced to the dental profession. This drove a revolving bit through a flexible shaft and enabled the drill to be applied at any desired angle, while the operator retained complete control. Even so drilling was still tedious and tired the operator's hands quickly.

The efficiency of cutting was further improved by using mechanical means to rotate the drill more quickly and power-fully yet still allowing it to reach points inaccessible to the straight instrument. Many drill-stocks were invented, for example McDowall's, which used the principle of the ARCHI-MEDEAN SCREW (like a spiral ratchet, or pump screwdriver), and Chevalier's, with a hand-cranked gear system, both of which could produce about 300 revolutions per minute (rpm). Clockwork motors were also tried.

In the 1870s the dental treadle foot drill was introduced where the rotary power was transmitted via a cable arm to a handpiece which held the drill bit or bur and instrument speeds were advanced to 700 rpm. As electricity became more commonplace over the next 50 years the electric 'engine' (ELECTRIC MOTOR), first available in the late 1870s, was only gradually accepted into general practice as a safe and reliable innovation and provided operating speeds of up to 1000 rpm. The speed of the engine was varied by a foot-operated control, and the rotary power of the motor was transmitted to the hand-piece by an endless belt or cord running over pulleys on a three-part extension cord arm. This method can still be seen in use today in modified form. The handpieces were interchangeable and enabled the burs to be set at any desired angle with respect to the handle of the instrument.

A wide range of shapes and sizes of burs were made and these could be sharpened again after use. Other instruments were also developed, including carborundum moulded into round cylindrical shapes mounted upon steel shafts, and discs and brushes. By 1920 some advanced electric dental engines were capable of up to 4000 rpm, but these were rare and the steel burs then available quickly became blunt at such speeds.

At this stage the dental drill was still inefficient when judged by its ability to remove tooth substance quickly and without effort. Dental drilling was noisy and still time-consuming and tiring. Even with perfect local anaesthesia ensuring that the operation can be carried out painlessly, the vibration and noise of inefficient drilling on the teeth is conducted via the bones of the jaws directly to the hearing apparatus set in the bone of

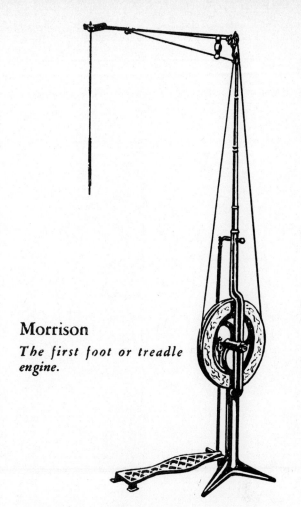

EASTMAN DENTAL HOSPITAL

Morrison
The first foot or treadle engine.

Above: the first treadle operated dental drill from 1872. This device gave the dental surgeon much greater freedom than had hitherto been possible. Such devices are still manufactured for use in areas where electricity may not be readily available.

Below: various ingenious devices were invented for drilling teeth. Many designs were based on much older tools, such as the carpenter's brace. Here are two early types of dental drill which operate on the archimedean screw principle like the 'pump' screwdriver.

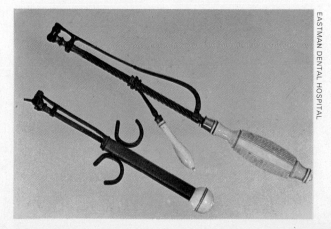

EASTMAN DENTAL HOSPITAL

the skull and seemingly amplified. Burs, which are milling devices, remove chips of tooth substance, and bounce and chatter at low speeds. The dental drill, which now gave the dental surgeon the technical capacity to carry out restorations of the teeth far beyond that possible without it, was still the feared and detested symbol of dentistry. People's reactions to dental treatment have always been directly and negatively influenced by the length of time that has to be spent using the dental drill to prepare their teeth.

In 1942 the first diamond instruments were produced. These were precision steel shafts and discs to which diamond abrasive powder was firmly attached. They were found to perform

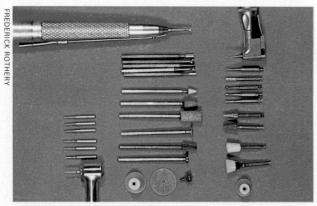

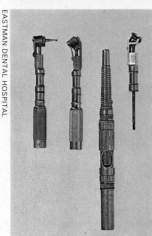

Above: various modern drill handpieces with a selection of burs and polishing devices. In the top left hand corner is a handpiece with directed water jet cooler attached.

Left: different heads can be attached to the handpieces, providing a number of drill angles and extensions. These drills are cable and belt driven by an electric motor.

Below: this early drill mechanism is clockwork driven. It was superseded by the foot-powered treadle drill.

better at speeds in excess of 2000 rpm, and at 6000 rpm the vibration and noise were reduced and a lighter touch was possible with reduction of tension for both the operator and his patient. Treatment became speedier and more extensive tooth preparations could be considered.

By 1947 much tougher tungsten carbide burs were available and now speeds of up to 12,000 rpm could be used. Handpieces had to be made with even greater precision and with adequate provision for lubrication of the fast-moving metal-to-metal parts. At the same time the problem of heat production in the tooth was overcome by arranging that a stream of cooling water should play over the surface being cut.

The next step forward was the introduction of the ball-bearing handpiece in 1953 with speeds of up to 25,000 rpm. Ducts were now being incorporated into some handpiece heads to convey coolant sprays more accurately to the cut surfaces. Even higher speeds can now be obtained with gear systems included in the drive mechanisms to the handpieces.

The air-turbine drill In 1957, after over a decade of research and development, the first air-driven turbine handpieces became available and they transformed modern operative dentistry by providing a free-running speed of 300,000 rpm. In 1962 this was even further improved by the use of air-BEARINGS to 800,000 rpm. It was found that operating speeds in excess of 250,000 rpm were above the level of vibratory perception of the patient, who was only aware of a whistling noise as his teeth were drilled.

The principle of the dental air-turbine is that a foot-controlled flow of compressed air is carried via a flexible hose to the handpiece where it is directed against the blade of a miniature air-turbine, causing it to spin. The air is exhausted partially from the head of the handpiece, returning through a tube back to the control box. An oil mist is introduced into the compressed air to provide constant lubrication of the turbine motor. An air and water bur coolant is also conducted by a concentric tube to be blown accurately upon the bur from jets in the head of the headpiece. The bur, of diamond abrasive or tungsten carbide, is held in the central shaft of the turbine by a friction grip chuck and is easily interchangeable, although each shape of instrument is more versatile and long-lasting at these ultra-high speeds.

The cutting efficiency of the air-turbine is outstanding. A very light pressure is used and the hard tooth substance gently wiped away. If the pressure on the tooth is in excess of 5 to 6 ounces (140 to 170 grammes) the engine slows and stalls. The ultra-speed air-turbine is used for rapid removal of bulky amounts of tooth substance while the relatively slower high-speed drills are used for other purposes such as finishing the cavity surfaces. Rotary instruments are still used at low speeds for slow removal of decayed tooth in circumstances where the operator's sense of touch is needed, and they are also employed for polishing.

Recent developments Air-motors have now been developed where the turbine is larger and has a greater torque, or turning-power, so that burs can be used at slower and more conventional speeds powered by the same compressed-air source as the air-turbine. Miniature lightweight electric motors held in the hand are obtainable and these have great versatility and increased mechanical efficiency because they do not require a drive transmission to the handpiece. Finger-tip engine controls and methods of conducting light to the working area in the mouth via a FIBRE OPTIC system incorporated into the handpiece head have also been studied.

DRILL, electric

The electric drill is a portable drilling machine, powered by its own electric motor carried in the case. Apart from the motor, the essential components are the *chuck*, which holds the drill, and a simple gear train, for gearing the speed of the motor down to a suitable speed for the drill.

The domestic electric drill usually takes the shape of a pistol, the 'pistol grip' being a good example of ERGONOMIC DESIGN, that is, correctly designed for easy usage. The power cord enters the case at the base of the grip, and the on-off switch is the 'trigger'. Often an interlock is provided so that the 'trigger' need not be held down continuously while using the drill. On larger, heavier models there are other handles on the case as well as the grip, so that both hands can safely be used to bring pressure on the work. The other handle may be a simple bar extending from the case at the top, opposite the grip, or may be a stirrup at the back end of the case, opposite the chuck.

The chuck

The chuck is a three-jawed self-centring device which protrudes from the gearbox end of the case and holds the drill. Turning the outer sleeve of the chuck in an anti-clockwise direction opens the jaws; the other direction closes it, final tightening being achieved with the use of a key supplied.

The motor

Housed in the case is an electric motor of the *series* or *universal* type. The advantages of this type of motor are that it is suitable for use with either DC or AC current, and that it produces a high torque at low speeds: as one pushes harder while drilling, thus increasing the load, the speed decreases but the torque increases. The gear train reduces the speed to about 2500 rev/min.

A disadvantage of this type of motor is that it provides interference with nearby radio and TV reception; this can be overcome by fitting various chokes and capacitors to the motor circuitry.

Electrical safety

For safety, electric power tools are either *earthed* or *double insulated*; tools with plastic bodies are double insulated.

Earthed tools are fitted with three-core power cable. The green-yellow conductor is connected to all the metal parts which may be touched by the operator and must be fitted at the other end to the earth [ground] pin of a suitable plug. The

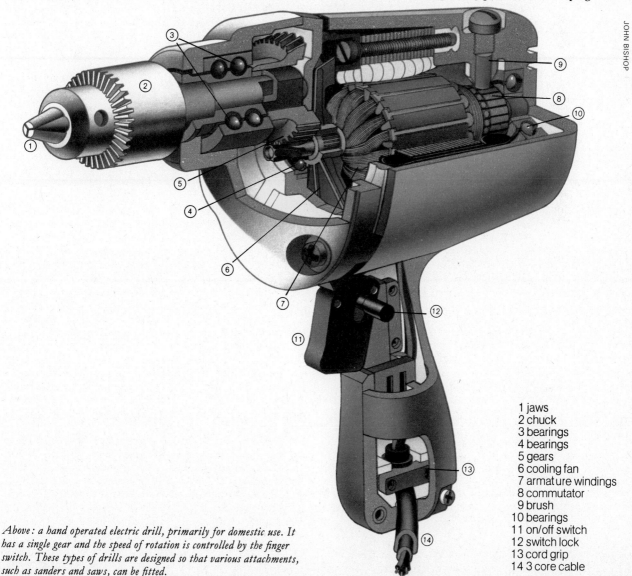

Above: a hand operated electric drill, primarily for domestic use. It has a single gear and the speed of rotation is controlled by the finger switch. These types of drills are designed so that various attachments, such as sanders and saws, can be fitted.

1 jaws
2 chuck
3 bearings
4 bearings
5 gears
6 cooling fan
7 armature windings
8 commutator
9 brush
10 bearings
11 on/off switch
12 switch lock
13 cord grip
14 3 core cable

socket outlet must be earthed to make this protection effective.

Double-insulated tools should be clearly marked as such, and are provided with two-core cable. The first (*functional*) insulation is the same as found in any electric tool; the secondary insulation is able to withstand a much higher test voltage than the functional insulation, so that the operator is protected from any breakdown causing leakage of current.

Drills, applications and attachments

Drill bits are normally of the twist-drill type, having two helical grooves

Below: two types of electric drill. In the top photo, the chuck of the portable electric drill is tightened with the key provided. In the lower picture, a machine tool drills holes in steel. Such a machine has a variable speed range, adjustable according to the size of the hole and the hardness of the material to be drilled. The drill bit is installed in the chuck by means of tapered sleeves with tangs; other types of cutting tools can also be used.

running from the twin cutting edges for about three-quarters of the length, the remainder being plain shank for inserting into the chuck. The capacity of electric drills ranges from $\frac{1}{4}$ inch (6.35 mm) to $\frac{1}{2}$ inch (12.7 mm). Sizes larger than $\frac{1}{2}$ inch are usually difficult to handle in a portable tool.

An electric drill with a given capacity is designed to handle a drilling job of that size in drilling metal; a drill bit of a larger size, with a cut-down shank to fit the chuck, may be used with caution to drill wood or plastic. Caution is always necessary when drilling metal. Certain types of steel may need a very hard cutting edge, a specially ground angle on the cutting edge, lubrication while drilling, or all three. When drilling a hole all the way through a piece of metal, the pressure brought to bear must be carefully applied as the bit goes through, otherwise the emerging bit may 'grab' the rough edge of the hole, giving the tool a severe wrench which can cause loss of control.

Two-speed and percussion electric drills are also available. The first provides a lower alternative speed of about 900 rev/min; the second gives a percussive effect combined with low speed, and is designed for use on concrete and masonry. Because of the abrasive nature of concrete and masonry, drill bits with specially hardened cutting edges must be used.

The versatility of the electric drill is extended by the availability of attachments designed to make use of the rotary motion, such as rotary files, sanding discs, hole saws, grindstones, and so on. An electric drill is often designed to be fitted, if desired, to a bench or table-mounted machine, to turn it into a drill-press or a lathe attachment for great precision or certain applications, such as use with a jig or fixture which can be attached to the table.

DRILLING RIG, oil

The first producing oil well was drilled in Pennsylvania, in 1859. Since then over two million bore holes have been sunk worldwide. Many of these have failed to find commercial quantities of oil, as opposed to the exceptionally productive few. Drilling is a very expensive business, and a costly gamble too; hence the importance of preliminary geological surveys.

Offshore oil wells are more expensive than those on land, but they are not basically different. Most of the world's oil wells have so far been drilled on land but now, partly because most of the likely land areas have already been explored, drilling at sea is increasingly important. Drilling for oil has been described as analogous to a dentist drilling a tooth with his patient the length of a football field away. This gives an idea of the problem involved in controlling from the surface a drill at the bottom of a well up to 8 km (5 miles) deep.

The drill string and bit

Oil drilling is done by rotating a drilling bit to make a hole. The bit may be a fishtailed steel one for soft ground, but it is usually a rotary bit with hardened teeth. In very hard rock, diamond or tungsten carbide teeth are used and it may take an hour to drill 2.5 cm (1 inch). (In softer rock, however, rates of about 100 metres (or yards) per hour are possible.) The bit is fixed to a 'string' of drill pipes which rotate it as it bores the hole. Each length of pipe is normally 9 m (30 ft) long and about 11 cm (4$\frac{1}{2}$ inch) or 14 cm (5$\frac{1}{2}$ inch) in diameter. The pipes are joined by heavy tapered threads. The pipes situated just above the bit are heavier than those in the rest of the string. They are called drill collars and are used to put enough weight on the drill to force it into the ground while keeping the rest of the drill string in tension. The whole of the drill string may weigh several hundred tons and if it were allowed to bear on the drill under compression the string could easily break or jam in the hole. In fact most of the weight of the drill string is taken by the drilling equipment on the surface.

Rotary drilling The most obvious part of the equipment on the surface is the derrick, looking rather like an electricity pylon and up to 60 m (200 ft) high. Its height is needed to hoist lengths of drill pipe into place, and to stack lengths of several drill pipes screwed together. The drill string is rotated in the well through a rotating table at the base of the derrick, driven at about 120 rev/min by a powerful motor. This rotating table has a central hole, through which a length of square or hexagonal pipe known as a *kelly* can slide and by which it can be turned. The kelly is the top section of the drill string and drives the rest of the string as it is turned by the rotary table. The drill string consisting of the kelly, pipes and bit is suspended on a hook from the top of the derrick by cables and pulleys. As the bit cuts into the ground, the kelly slides through the hole in the rotary table. When the bit has descended almost the length of the kelly the drill string is wedged in place, the kelly is disconnected, a new length of drill pipe is added to the string, the

Above: the first well dug by 'Colonel' Drake at Titusville, Pennsylvania, USA, in 1859. The rig was adapted from those used for water, and oil was found at the shallow depth of 69 ft (21 m).

Below: an offshore drilling rig for oil exploration in Australia.

kelly is reconnected, and drilling begins again.

This operation will have to be carried out over 600 times in drilling a 6000 m (20,000 ft) well. Each time it is done a team of men have to carry out hard and exacting physical work in connecting and disconnecting pipes and wedges and taking new pipe out of the stack. Sheer hard work, as well as highly developed operating skill, is still a most essential part of oil drilling. As drilling continues the drill itself becomes blunt, perhaps after only a few hours if it is in hard rock. Then the whole drill string has to be taken out of the hole so that the bit can be removed and a new one put on. This 'round trip' can take up to a day to do. As the drill pipe comes up it is unscrewed in lengths of three, not in single joints, to speed up operations.

During drilling, specially prepared 'mud', a complex colloidal suspension, usually in water, is pumped down the drill pipes through a jet in the bit, and back to the surface in the annular space between the drill pipe and the sides of the hole. This space exists because the diameter of the drill is always larger than the diameter of the drill pipe. The mud circulates through the well quite slowly and cools and lubricates the drill. It also flushes drillings up to the surface, where they are separated from the mud, which is then re-used. In returning to the surface, the mud coats the side of the hole and helps to keep it from caving in. The mud also helps to control any flow of oil or gas from the well. The weight of the column of mud is generally greater than any likely pressure of oil or gas, so that the oil cannot get to the surface until the weight of mud is reduced. In early wells, before mud was used, any oil or gas found under pressure shot at once to the surface, causing a *gusher* which was both difficult to get under control and liable to catch fire.

Another method always used in modern wells to prevent uncontrolled flow is a *blow out preventer*. This is an arrangement of heavy rubber-tipped pistons that can be hydraulically closed to shut off the well entirely. The blow out preventer is firmly fixed to the top of a steel casing that is inserted into the well and cemented in place as the well goes down. Depending on the tendency of the strata to crumble, and the drilling programme, casing may be continued all or only part of the way down the hole.

When oil is found the first indication is usually from hydrocarbon analysis of the drilling mud returning to the surface. The oil is tested for quality and flow rate and, if this is satisfactory, production tubing is cemented in and a 'Christmas Tree', so called because of a resemblance in shape of the complex of valves and tubing that makes it up, is fixed at the well head.

An alternative to rotary drilling is turbo drilling, where the drill is driven at the bottom of the well by a turbine operated by the drilling mud or (electro drilling) by an electric motor. Rotary drilling, however, is still by far the most usual method.

Offshore drilling This is being done in many parts of the world, but the North Sea is one of the most active areas for exploration, at the present time. It is also the most difficult area so far explored, because of adverse weather conditions, and

Below left: modern rotary tri-cone jet bits. The bit is rotated under the weight of the drill collar to force the teeth into the rock. This also makes the cones rotate about their own axes and the teeth chip and crush the rock. Beneath the slight projection between each cone it is just possible to see the jet for the drilling mud.

Below: a rig showing the kelly, rotary table and drill pipes.

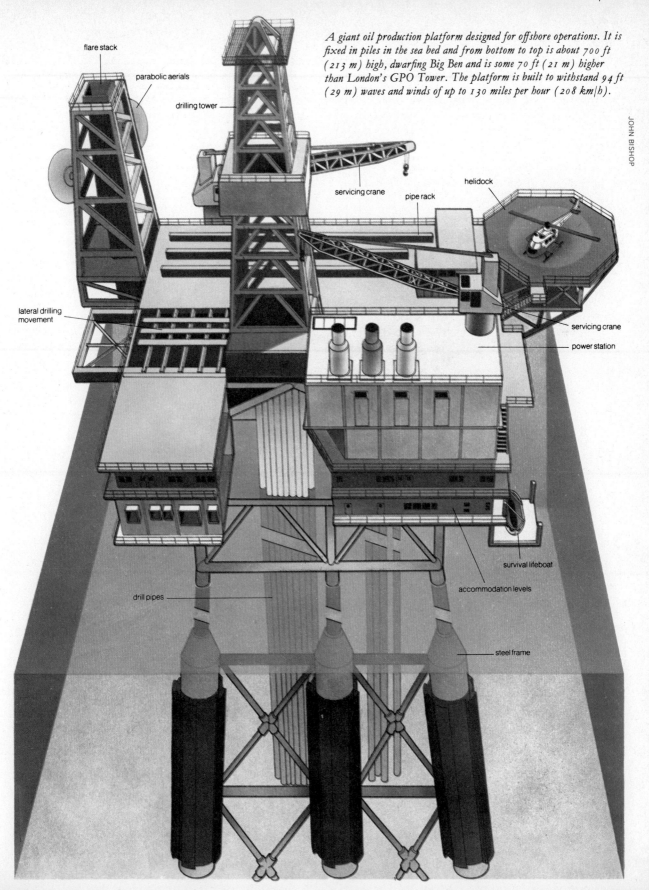

flare stack

parabolic aerials

drilling tower

servicing crane

pipe rack

helidock

A giant oil production platform designed for offshore operations. It is fixed in piles in the sea bed and from bottom to top is about 700 ft (213 m) high, dwarfing Big Ben and is some 70 ft (21 m) higher than London's GPO Tower. The platform is built to withstand 94 ft (29 m) waves and winds of up to 130 miles per hour (208 km/h).

JOHN BISHOP

lateral drilling movement

servicing crane

power station

survival lifeboat

accommodation levels

drill pipes

steel frame

the distance from the coast of most of the fields. Drilling has been going on for gas and oil in the North Sea since the early 1960s, but this has been in comparatively shallow water. At present intensive oil drilling is being carried out in deeper water, under more difficult circumstances. Fortunately the whole of the North Sea is shallow compared with the oceans; much of it is between 30 m (100 ft) and 200 m (650 ft) deep. This is typical of the so-called continental shelf areas which make up about 10% of the world's under-sea surface.

Types of marine platforms

To support the drilling rig, ancillary equipment and crew's quarters, some form of floating platform is needed. The first wells were drilled from converted ships, and these are still in use, but a limiting factor is their tendency to drag even the heaviest anchors during rough weather. Fixed or self-contained platforms are used in shallow water, to a depth of about 30 m (100 ft). Another type of rig is the self-elevating (jack-up) platform, which has an operational limit of 90 m (300 ft), or so, because of bending stress in the leg supports. They can be towed into position and the legs jacked down until they stand on the sea bottom and then further jacked until the platform is well above the sea surface, clear of the heaviest waves. The most recent development in offshore drilling has been the use of *semisubmersible rigs*. These have several large hulls with long legs holding a platform above them, and the hulls are ballasted so as to sink about 20 m (65 ft) below the surface of the water. As with jack-up rigs, the platform is still well above the water and clear of the waves. The rig may be held in place by multiple anchors or it may be dynamically positioned. In this method, multiple propulsion

Below left: an exploratory drilling rig. If the drilling mud appears to be disappearing below ground this is a sign of porous rock and possibly oil, gas, or water. There must be at least one of these as there are no empty spaces deep in the Earth's crust.

units on the rig respond to signals from a beacon on the sea bottom and keep the rig exactly in position in relation to the beacon, even in the worst weather.

At the hull level a semisubmersible may be about 60 m (200 ft) wide by 76 m (250 ft) long, and its operating draught will be 18 m (60 ft) to 27 m (90 ft). One rig could cost up to £10 million [$24 million]. The biggest semisubmersible in the North Sea at the end of 1973 could drill to a depth of 10,000 m (33,000 ft) in up to 300 m (1000 ft) of water. It could survive in winds of up to 220 km/h (136 mile/h) and in waves of up to 26 m (85 ft). Even larger semisubmersibles are currently being built.

Producing wells After exploration drill rigs have been used to find oil they are moved on to other areas for further exploration. In order to drill producing wells, production platforms are installed. These enormous steel or concrete platforms stand on the sea bottom and, by angling the hole using a technique known as directional drilling, up to 30 producing wells can be drilled from each platform. Oil is treated on the platform to remove gas and water and is brought ashore by pipeline or by tanker. Plans are also being made to drill producing wells and take oil from them without a production platform, working on the sea floor from wellhead cellars serviced by pressure vessels from the surface. A system of this kind has been used to drill and service a well in the Gulf of Mexico in 114 m (375 ft) of water, and a North Sea trial of this system is planned for 1975. This undersea technique could show great savings compared to drilling only from platforms but it will probably supplement rather than replace the production platform.

Below: a semisubmersible oil and gas drilling rig, Sedco 135, searching for gas (often found with oil) in the Maui gas field, New Zealand. Gas flaring is a routine part of testing to determine the quality, quantity and pressure of any gas found in a well.

DRILL, pneumatic

Popularly (and incorrectly) known as a 'pneumatic drill', the pneumatic paving breaker is percussive, that is, it has a hammering action, as opposed to a drill which is either entirely rotary or rotary and percussive in action. As its name implies, the pneumatic breaker is powered by compressed air, which imparts a hammer action to the tool which it holds, enabling it to do a variety of jobs, such as breaking up road surfaces, demolishing buildings, digging trenches, and even hammering down sheet steel piling, using interchangeable tool bits.

The pneumatic paving breaker is a relatively modern invention, replacing other methods of breaking solid surfaces like the pickaxe or the hammer and wedge, which are both time-consuming. The breaker is a T-shaped machine ruggedly constructed in forged steel, in a variety of weights to suit particular job requirements. The main part is a vertical cylinder with handles and throttle control across the top. Compressed air is fed in through a flexible hose from a COMPRESSOR to the top of the cylinder, below the handle, and is conducted alternately to each end of a sliding piston via a valve. As the compressed air released by the throttle lever first enters the upper cylinder, the piston is forced down on to a cylindrical sliding anvil, beneath which is the working tool (chisel, wedge, asphalt cutter, or spade, for example).

The energy of the piston hitting the anvil forces it on to the tool, which is in turn struck down on to the working surface. After striking the anvil, the piston is driven back to the top of the cylinder by compressed air entering the lower end and forcing it upwards. Following both the upward and downward movements of the piston, the compressed air is exhausted to the atmosphere in a downwards direction.

In order to conduct the compressed air to the upper and lower parts of the cylinder, valves and ducts are built into the body, and since minimum wear on the moving anvil and piston is essential, the compressed air is normally lubricated by an oil valve in the throttle mechanism, fed from a reservoir below the handle which holds enough oil for about eight hours' work. Further reduction in wear can be achieved by the design of air 'cushions' at the top and bottom of the cylinder to prevent the piston from hitting the ends of the cylinder during its operation.

Pneumatic paving breakers operate on compressed air at a pressure of about 85 psi (6 bar) and vary in consumption according to size from 40 to 75 cu ft (1.1 to 2.1 m³) of air per minute, producing between 1100 and 1500 blows per minute, again according to size and type.

Noise reduction
Vibration and noise are inherent with much pneumatic equipment, not least with pneumatic breakers, but attempts have been made to embody various forms of recoil damping, similar to the telescopic forks of a MOTORCYCLE, for the greater comfort of the operators. Many makers now provide integral plastic silencers which considerably reduce the low-frequency exhaust noise which is so irritating to people living or working nearby. The high-frequency 'chatter' of the piston-anvil-tool combination and of the tool hitting the working surface is more difficult to silence, although this problem has been partly solved by fitting a steel-covered rubber collar around the shank of the tool.

Right: a hand operated pneumatic breaker. As the hand lever is depressed compressed air flows into the outer compartment, down and under the piston. The piston rises compressing the air above it and forcing the diaphragm valve open. Air can now enter the area above the piston initiating the down stroke.

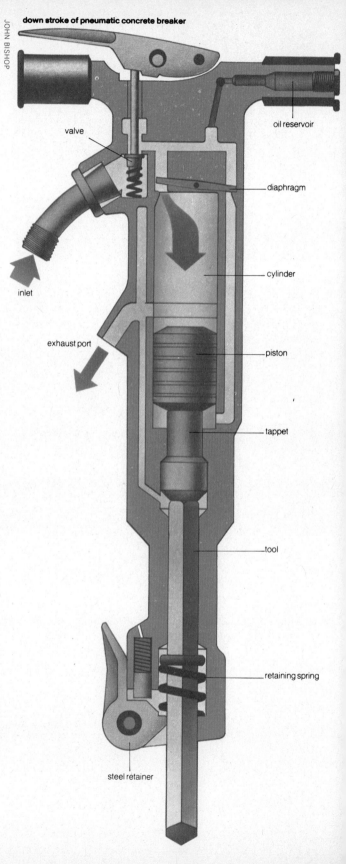

JOHN BISHOP

down stroke of pneumatic concrete breaker

oil reservoir

valve

diaphragm

cylinder

inlet

exhaust port

piston

tappet

tool

retaining spring

steel retainer

JOHN LAING & SON LTD

COLORIFIC

Above left: pneumatic breakers are widely used in demolition work. When concrete flooring is being removed it is cut into sections which can be lifted away by a hoist or crane, as in this picture. When reinforced concrete flooring has to be removed the sections are cut parallel to the line of the main reinforcement.

Above right: one of the most common uses of pneumatic breakers is for digging up roads. The noise produced is a frequent source of irritation to people in the area around, and the breaker in this picture is fitted with a sound absorbing jacket which reduces its noise level. The compressors used to power the road breakers are also considerably quieter today than they were several years ago.

Right: pneumatic rock drills are used in quarrying to cut the holes into which the explosive charges, usually dynamite or gelignite, are placed.

ZEFA

DRIVING SIMULATOR

The fully equipped driving simulator faithfully reproduces the 'feel' of the accelerator, brakes, steering and gear shift of a modern car while at the same time requiring the pupil under instruction to 'drive' along a realistically contrived roadway, complete with moving traffic and all types of hazards. The 'car' is, however, mounted on a static platform in the driving school and the 'roadway' is a film, photographed through the windscreen of an actual car in motion. The simulator thus enables the pupil both to practise driving techniques and to get the 'feel' of a real car in a variety of situations.

Each driving action is electronically monitored at the instructor's desk and the instructor can impose various situations on the student driver, thus testing both his reactions and adaptability, while at the same time equipping him with realistic experience so that he can cope with actual road conditions.

The student's driving position is in an accurate replica of a modern car, with steering wheel, speedometer, trafficator (indicator) lever, automatic or manual gear change, hand and foot brakes, clutch, accelerator, headlamp switch with dip, oil pressure gauge or warning light and rear view mirrors. In addition, an 'error' panel is fitted, showing the student immediately if he has stalled the engine, is driving with the handbrake on, exceeding the speed limit or, in conjunction with actual situations shown on the film, braking or steering too hard or insufficiently to meet the situation before him. Another illuminated panel shows the student which gear is engaged so as to assist him in selecting the correct gear at the proper time and speed. Each car has a 'stalling' speed and the pupil cannot continue to drive in a high gear if the related engine speed is too low. Similarly, the clutch, which incorporates a built-in friction device to simulate taking up the load, must be properly operated at each gear change.

A 'castor' action is included in the steering mechanism to provide a simulated feel of the wheels on the road, and the feel of light, medium and hard braking is also provided.

Up to 32 simulators can be connected to the instructor's central console, where all of the essential actions of each pupil are monitored by computer in conjunction with a binary code on the sound track of the film. All 'error' panel indications are repeated to the instructor, who is thus able to observe the actions—and progress—of each pupil, all of whose improper responses are individually accumulated on a digital counter. The instructor can insert a speed limit into each simulator. For example, if he decides that a certain situation requires a 20 mile/h (32 km/h) limit, he can switch this requirement into the system and the error panel will show to both the pupil and instructor if this limit is exceeded. Reversing and parking techniques can be practised by means of mirrors which,

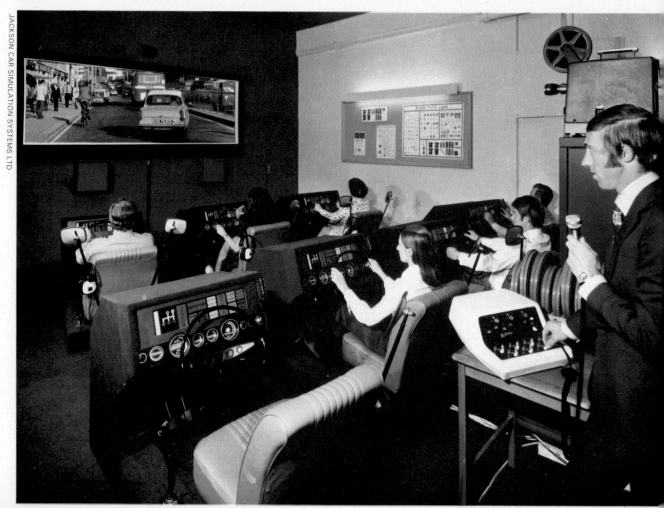

JACKSON CAR SIMULATION SYSTEMS LTD

combined with photographic projection techniques, represent the view the pupil would have when looking over his shoulder.

A separate printed readout can be provided of each pupil's performance throughout the test.

The films simulating driving in traffic were shot, in colour, through the windscreen of a car on journeys through moving traffic, and were edited to incorporate hazards of all types. Display is on a wide screen so that the pupil is not distracted by off-screen events. Several such films provide variety, and special films to illustrate particular aspects of driving are available. The film can be accompanied by an instructional commentary and can be stopped, reversed and re-run by the instructor at will to emphasize special or disregarded events.

Below left: a roomful of students using a driving simulator system. The system uses a 16 mm projector and a set of nine films; the student must operate the controls to conform with what is shown on the screen. Error lights on the student's panel glow with variable intensity according to the magnitude of the error. Each student's chair is equipped with mirrors for simulating reversal; the student sees the screen in the mirror and the film is projected in reverse.

Below: another approach to driving simulation. In this system, the way the student handles the controls affects what happens on the screen. This system features a gearbox and noise simulator.

P.S.J. CONTROLS

DRYCLEANING

Drycleaning, like so many other benefits of modern living, was discovered by accident. The discovery was made by a French dyeworks owner, Jean-Baptiste Jolly, who made the discovery in Paris in 1825, as a result of a simple accident. A maid in the Jolly household upset a paraffin [kerosene] lamp on a tablecloth. Jolly was amazed to discover that the area over which the paraffin had spilled was so clear that it showed up the dirtiness of the rest of the cloth. Operating from his dyeworks, he offered this new discovery as 'drycleaning' to distinguish it from the soap and water process previously used to clean fabrics.

At the time of the discovery of the drycleaning process, all garments were made from natural fibres such as wool, cotton, and so on which swelled when immersed in water and shrunk on drying. The French public realized the value of drycleaning when they found that garments could be totally immersed in the inert solvent and thoroughly cleaned without distortion through shrinkage. By using the new cleaning process, dirt ingrained over many years was gently floated away. Drycleaning spread to other countries where it was at first known as 'French Cleaning' because of its origin, and as it developed into an industry the first crude solvent, paraffin [kerosene] was replaced by benzine (an aliphatic petroleum hydrocarbon not to be confused with the aromatic compound, benzene, spelt with an 'e') and later by white spirit, which still survives in many countries as a cleaning solvent. In the USA a controlled quality white spirit called Stoddard solvent is widely used.

Benzine has a flash point of 32°F (0°C) and the fire risk involved reduced its attraction as a cleaning solvent; white spirit in the controlled form as Stoddard solvent has a flash point of 100°F (38°C) and is very much safer. The flash point is described as the temperature at which the solvent gives off a vapour which is flammable or explosive in the air immediately over the solvent.

Solvents used today When the drycleaning moved out of its factory-based environment into local shopping areas a non-flammable solvent was required. The first of these to be established was *trichloroethylene* ($CCl_2:CHCl$), a powerful solvent which is an efficient cleaner. The introduction of clothing made from triacetate rayon, which could be affected by this solvent, caused a general change to *perchloroethylene* ($CCl_2:CCl_2$), which is suitable for most garments brought to the drycleaner. Known as 'Perk', it quickly became established and is still the most widely used solvent in automatic drycleaning machines as displayed in 'on the spot' unit cleaners.

Fashion fabrics are subject to continuous change; some of the new fabrics and trimmings on sale are heat sensitive and some are sensitive even to perchloroethylene. This class of fabrics can be handled in a fluorinated solvent in the Freon range (these are used widely as refrigerants), called solvent 113. It will dry at a low safe temperature and being a gentle solvent is suitable for delicate fabrics. There is a further fluorinated hydrocarbon solvent '11' used in some continental European countries, which has a similar low-temperature drying facility as 113 but its solvency power is near to perchloroethylene.

To help the public and drycleaners through the difficulties of identifying fabrics and suitable cleaning treatment, clothes are frequently labelled with advice in the form of symbols.

Drycleaning process In response to the public demand for a cleaning service conveniently sited in the local high street, the machine manufacturers began to develop machines which would complete the whole drycleaning operation as sequential

PHOTOS: ALAN MARSHALL

processes (cleaning, drying, aerating, and so on), producing the garments ready for inspection, spotting (stain removal) and finishing.

Perk is a very suitable solvent for use in such automatic machines. The solvency strength of KB 90 is adequate for cleaning without being too severe. The action of the solvent is to dissolve grease, and drycleaning works because most of the soil on the garments is composed of dirt particles associated with oily matter by which the particles become attached to the fabric. The solvent dissolves the grease and thus the dirt particles are loosened. This process is assisted by the agitation of the perforated rotating drum, in which the articles are placed, until all the dirt is removed. Not all the dirt on garments can be removed by the solvent and a small percentage of water-carrying detergents are added to the solvent to remove water-

Left: the operator introduces a punched card into the machine and throws a switch to start the drycleaning cycle. The card is punched according to the process required, and initiates microswitches which control motors, the opening and closing of valves and so on. In this way the machine can be programmed to deal with a delicate white load, a heavy load, one that requires retexturing, short or long drying cycles, the number of solvent rinses and spinning times. The cycles can, however, be operated manually. The gauges indicate drying temperature, filter pressures and the steam pressure.

drycleaning symbols

(A) drycleanable in all drycleaning solvent

(P) drycleanable in perchloroethylene, white spirit and solvent 113

(F) drycleanable in white spirit or solvent 113 only

(X) not drycleanable

comparison of drycleaning solvents

property	white spirit	trichloro-ethylene (TRI)	perchloro-ethylene (PERK)	trichlorotri-fluoroethane (solvent 113)	monofluorotri-chloromethane (solvent 11)
boiling temperature distillation	302–392°F 150–200°C vacuum distillation necessary	188.4°F 86.9°C	250°F 121.1°C	117°F 47.57°C	75°F 23.8°C
Kauri-Butanol value (KB) indication of solvency power	31	130	90	30	60
toxicity maximum concentration permissable in parts per million this may vary slightly with local regulations	500	100	100	1000	1000
indication of volatility ease of drying the higher the number, the lower the temperature and time required to dry	difficult	84	39	170	223
flash point temperature at which solvent gives off vapour flammable in air	93°F	non-flam	non-flam	non-flam	non-flam

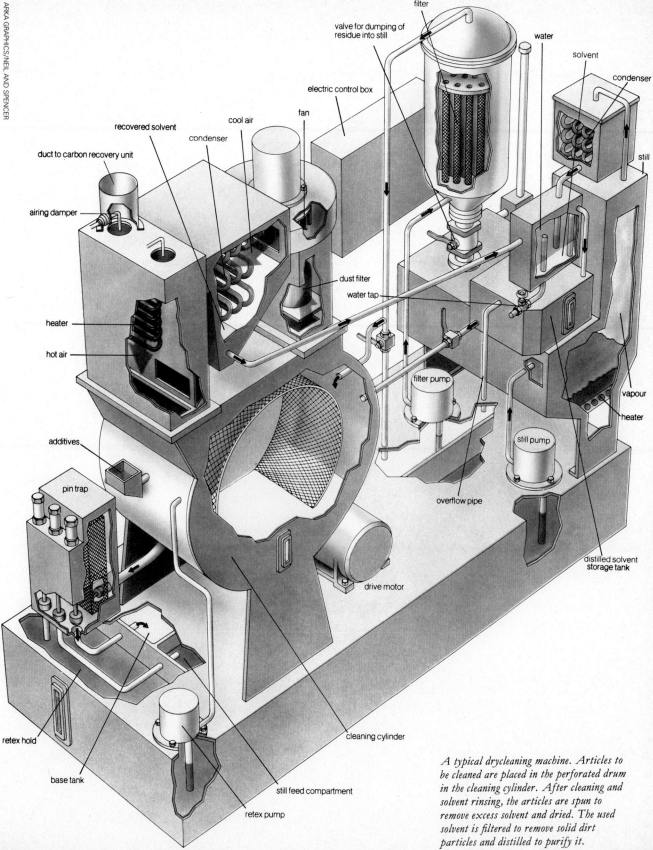

filter

valve for dumping of
residue into still

water

electric control box

solvent

condenser

fan

still

cool air

condenser

recovered solvent

duct to carbon recovery unit

airing damper

heater

hot air

dust filter

water tap

vapour

heater

additives

filter pump

pin trap

still pump

overflow pipe

distilled solvent
storage tank

drive motor

retex hold

base tank

still feed compartment

cleaning cylinder

retex pump

*A typical drycleaning machine. Articles to
be cleaned are placed in the perforated drum
in the cleaning cylinder. After cleaning and
solvent rinsing, the articles are spun to
remove excess solvent and dried. The used
solvent is filtered to remove solid dirt
particles and distilled to purify it.*

soluble dirt such as food and beverage stains. After cleaning and solvent rinsing, the garments are spun at high speed to extract excess solvent, followed by the drying process in which the clothes are gently tumbled in warm air.

The used solvent is then filtered to remove the solid dirt particles, followed by distillation to remove the soluble contaminants, thus the solvent is continuously purified for re-use. Perk distils easily in a simple vessel similar in operation to a kettle—unlike white spirit which requires to be distilled in a vacuum. A simple water-cooled condenser transforms the vapour into liquid solvent. Garments (especially woollen ones) hold small amounts of water; this comes off during drying and distillation. The purpose of the water separator is to act as a settling tank and it is constructed to take advantage of the wide difference in specific gravity between the solvent and the water. Because the unwanted water is lighter than the solvent and does not mix with it, it rises to the top and can be drained off before the solvent passes to the storage tank; the solvent from the drying section is similarly passed through the water separator.

After cleaning and drying is complete, the air in the machine has still some solvent content. Before the garments are unloaded, this solvent-laden air is exhausted to a carbon solvent recovery tower, which adsorbs (attracts to the surface of a solid) the solvent vapour in the same manner as a hood over a cooking stove adsorbs smells. Even this adsorbed solvent is recovered.

Additives to provide water repellency, moth proofing, and so on can be included in the process. They are added in small amounts to the solvent as part of a one-stage or, more frequently, two-stage cycle. Here the bulk of the dirt is removed by the first 'washing' and the second solvent wash provides the additive treatment. The most common of such additives is retexturing, which is a wax-based product introduced to restore to the garment the type of feel it had when new.

A new system for the collection of drycleaning after hours. The garments are left and paid for at the shop and a magnetically coded card is handed over. When placed in the machine this activates a rail bringing the clothes out through an inner door which closes behind it before opening the outer door to the customer.

DUPLICATING

Duplicating, as opposed to copying (see PHOTOCOPYING and XEROGRAPHY), requires the preparation of a master sheet which makes duplicates on a machine. There are two main types of duplicating: *stencil* duplicating and *spirit* or *hectographic* duplicating. Both have been in use for nearly a century.

Stencil duplicating

This technique uses a master sheet on to which lettering is impressed as lines of perforations through which ink can be squeezed on to the copy paper. The first experiments with stencils tried different variations on a file plate process, which used a board or a plate with a rough surface on it similar to a file. A blunt stylus was used on a waxed stencil, placed over the file plate, to make a handwritten master. The first major improvement was made in 1882 with the introduction of the Cyclostyle pen by David Gestetner. This was a spiked wheel pen which could be used as for normal handwriting, but made a series of perforations in the stencil. A Japanese paper was imported which had long fibres, providing a firm yet porous base for the stencil. In the 1890s another Japanese paper proved suitable for making stencils on the TYPEWRITER, which by then was becoming widely used.

Automatic flatbed machines were patented in the 1890s for making stencil duplicates, and rotary machines were patented in 1896 by Lowe in the USA and Ellams in England. The first successful rotary machines were marketed early in the twentieth century. Gestetner, A B Dick, and Klaber (using the name Rotary Neostyle, later shortened to Roneo) all introduced rotary models, Gestetner using a twin-cylinder design. The materials have changed and the process has become less messy, but the principle has remained the same since then.

The stencil consists of a porous backing sheet and an ink-resisting coating, originally wax. The action of writing or typing on it (using a typewriter without a ribbon) pushed the wax out of the way, allowing the ink when applied to come through the porous backing on to the copy paper. The fibrous nature of the backing sheet retains the centre of letters like 'o' and 'a' so that their centres do not fill up with ink.

Early stencils required several sheets of different types to make a good typewritten impression. The process was messy and the machine had to be cranked by hand. The stencil could

Below: an early Roneo stencil duplicator, which works on the same principle as many modern machines—forcing ink through perforations in an impervious sheet on to the copy paper.

be used for only one short run. Modern stencils use a variety of plastics and can be used several times, although the quality of reproduction is still best on the first run. Modern machines are usually electric. The ink is applied from inside the drum, and some machines feature patented ink systems which can be removed and replaced so that different colours may be run.

Spirit duplicating This process is also called the hectographic method; the term hectographic came from the Greek word for 100 and it was originally claimed that 100 copies could be made. It is also called the ditto process, especially in the USA, and the ink was originally a purple colour. This colour has become strongly identified with the process although nowadays almost any colour can be used.

The method uses a strong aniline dye Originally the ink was transferred to a sheet of gelatin by placing the sheet of paper with the dye on it in a shallow tray. The moisture-retaining qualities of gelatin kept the ink moist, and the copy was made by pressing an ordinary sheet of paper on to the gelatin. A number of copies could be made before the ink became exhausted and a new master had to be made.

The modern process was developed in 1923 by the Ormig company in Germany. The master is in two parts, the lower one like a sheet of carbon paper with the dye on the top side; the dye is transferred to the back of the top sheet when it is typed or written upon. This sheet is then clipped to a revolving drum, and the sheets to be printed are moistened with a volatile fluid which dissolves a thin layer of dye on the master, thus transferring it to the clean paper. The process can continue until the dye on the master is exhausted. The modern process is

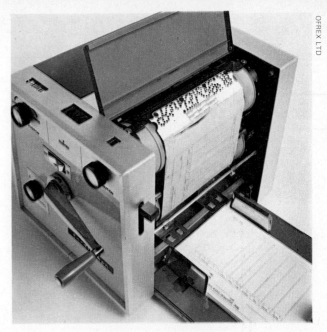

OFREX LTD

Above: a modern stencil duplicator, working in the same way as the one in the previous picture. The stencil can be seen inside the casing.

Below: a spirit duplicator, partly dismantled to show the spirit dispenser. The rubber wheels feed paper to the cylinder.

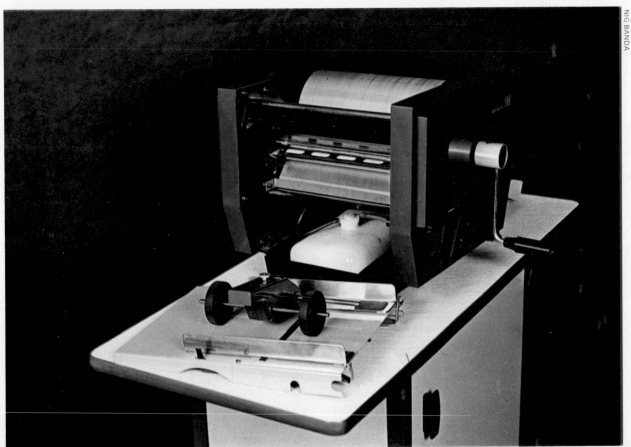

NIG BANDA

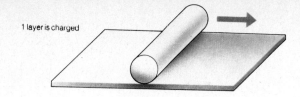

1 layer is charged

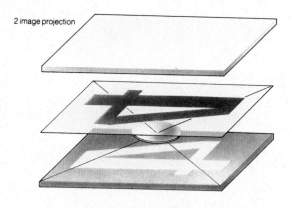

2 image projection

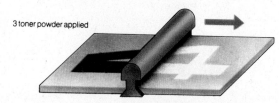

3 toner powder applied

4 paper layer

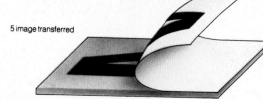

5 image transferred

6 fixing

Above: the xerographic process. A semiconducting plate is electrostatically charged. When an image is projected on to the surface only the darkened areas retain the charge and a fine powder dusted on will adhere to these. The 'image' can then be transferred to another piece of paper and fixed.

not messy because the carbon is not softened until in contact with the fluid.

Azograph This is a process patented by the A B Dick company, and available commercially in the USA. It is similar to spirit duplicating but uses different chemicals. The master includes two colour compounds which become visible when united in contact with a fluid. The compounds are united when the master is typed or written upon, and the fluid is applied in the machine.

Thermographic method This is a new method introduced commercially at the Business Efficiency Exhibition in 1973. It was developed by Rapid Data Ltd of Britain. The master is typed, forming a heat-absorbing black image on a white sheet. This is attached to a heated drum, and only the image reaches the critical temperature, the rest of the sheet remaining several degrees cooler. The drum makes contact with a continuous belt of waxed material which is highly pigmented. Some of the pigmented wax is melted by the heat on to the image and is then transferred to the copy sheet. The image is fixed and clean before it leaves the machine. The waxed sheets come in several colours and can be changed readily.

Below: a more complex spirit duplicator which uses a system of masks to blank out parts of the original master, so that differing versions of a document can be printed without having to type out each one separately on an individual master sheet.

Bottom: a stencil duplicator with (on the right) a thermal process stencil cutter, which makes a stencil from an ordinary typed document in a few seconds.

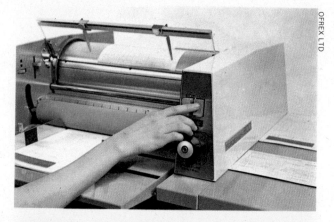

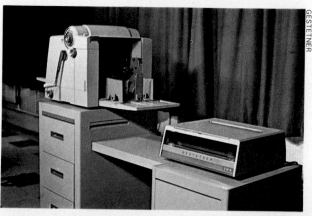

DYEING processes

Man's efforts to make himself and his surroundings more colourful date back to prehistoric times. He started to paint his body, either for adornment or for ritual purposes, long before he learned to make cloth from animal and vegetable fibres. His experiments over the course of thousands of years taught him how to obtain his colours from all kinds of sources, for example animals, plants and even the soil and rocks around him.

He found that although mixtures of finely ground minerals with oils or fats were useful as paints for his body and decorative work, their application to textiles was much less satisfactory. Because they were insoluble in water, the particles of colour could not penetrate into the interior of the fibres, and the adhesion of the paints to the surface of the fibres was comparatively poor. A textile dye must be soluble, even if only during the actual dyeing process.

Thus true dyeing, and not merely surface staining, depends on the ability of a dye to gain access to the interior of the fibre and stay there, either because of its chemical affinity for the fibre when the dye is soluble, or because of the inability of an insoluble colour particle to wander out again through the narrow capillary channels of the fibre during, say, washing.

Until far into the nineteenth century, only natural colouring agents were known, and very few of these were fast to light and washing, that is, they soon faded in sunlight or washed out too readily. Furthermore these colours were not very pure and not really brilliant.

The turning point came in 1855 when the Englishman, William Perkin, discovered the first synthetic dye *mauveine* from aniline, a COAL TAR product. This proved to be an im-

Top: dye pits at Fez, where the famous Moroccan leather is dyed. Fez gave its name to the red felt hat, the crimson dye for which was obtained from a berry grown locally and also used for the leather.

Bottom: a modern dispensary on the first floor of a dyehouse. This picture shows pairs of tanks fitted with high speed mixers, which are used for supplying dyes and chemicals to the production machines, dyeing manmade fibres on the floor below.

mediate success and started off the industrial countries of Europe on an era of intensive research which resulted in the discovery of thousands of dyes. These were synthesized from aniline, benzene, toluene, naphthalene, anthracene and other ingredients of coal tar.

Though the first synthetic dyes were more brilliant than any of the earlier dyes, their fastness to light and washing was still poor. They were highly satisfactory for animal fibres like wool and silk, but they washed out of cotton and linen too easily, even in cold water. This was because there was simply no affinity between the dyes and vegetable (cellulosic) fibres. When the fibres, however, had been *mordanted*, that is, treated with solutions of tannic acid and metal salts (sometimes used by themselves), the dyes became fixed and could no longer be washed out. This was because they had reacted with the mordants to form insoluble compounds that were retained in the fine capillary spaces of the fibres. Since many of the natural dyes had had to be made wash-fast by mordanting, this treatment was not new to dyers.

Because of their brilliance and high colour yield, this first group of synthetic dyes, the basic dyes (salts of organic bases which give bright colours), are still in use for colouring short-lived articles like matches, cheap paper, and so on, but find little application to textiles.

Azo dyes In 1858, Peter Gries discovered a reaction in which numerous organic compounds could be linked together by a nitrogen, or *azo*, bond —N=N—, to produce dyes that nowadays exist in their thousands. Those with an acidic nature and which readily dissolve in water are known as *acid dyes*; they combine with the basic component present in all animal fibres (proteins) to form a truly stable chemical compound. They have no affinity for cellulosic fibres.

Other azo dyes are highly suitable for cellulosic fibres, within which they are firmly held as large, sparingly soluble complexes when common salt or Glauber's salt (sodium sulphate) is added to the dye solution. They are very popular and are known as *substantive* or *direct dyes*. Over the years, the azo dyes have developed into highly light-fast products. Though their wash-fastness is moderate, especially at high temperatures, it can be improved by treating the dyed material with metal salts or other substances that enlarge the molecule, a step that usually reduces solubility.

Some acid dyes intended for wool have metals (for example chromium) incorporated in the molecule during their manufacture. These *metal complex dyes* have achieved outstanding light- and wash-fastness.

The azo dyes for cellulosic fibres can be rendered entirely water-insoluble by reacting their component parts together within the fibre itself. In this case, the fibre is treated with a solution of one of the components, the excess being either squeezed out or centrifuged. On adding the solution of the second component, the insoluble, highly fast dye is formed within the fibre. Commercially, these dyes are known as *azoic* dyes.

Vat dyes The *vat dyes* exhibit extraordinary fastness to light and washing when used for dyeing cellulosic fibres. This group also includes the well known natural dye *indigo* that has been in use for thousands of years. Indigo is now synthesized but its use is confined mainly to dyeing traditional non-fading blue denim (blue jeans) material. Modern vat dyes are mostly derived from anthracene and similar high-molecular-weight organic compounds. They are water-insoluble but can be made

temporarily soluble by treating with suitable chemicals. After dyeing, exposure to air or immersion in special baths renders these chemicals inactive and the insoluble vat dye is firmly embedded in the fibre.

Sulphur dyes

The *sulphur dyes* are soluble in the presence of sodium sulphide, which is inactivated after dyeing so that the once more insoluble dye is held in the cellulosic fibre. Though these dyes are not as brilliant and light-fast as the vat dyes, they are fast washing. The blacks and browns are mainly used.

Reactive dyes

The most recently developed dyes, the *reactive dyes*, are also very fast on cellulosic fibres and are produced by introducing a highly reactive group into soluble azo or anthracene dyes. This group combines chemically with cellulose. They compete strongly with vat dyes because of their brilliance, good fastness properties and ease of application.

Disperse dyes

The dyes mentioned so far are intended essentially for natural fibres, and still represent over 50% of world production. When regenerated cellulose fibres (rayon) were first produced from cotton linters and wood pulp at the beginning of the twentieth century, good results were obtained

Below left: removing cellular knitted blanket fabric after dyeing in a winch type machine. Fabric is dumped into the dye tank as a continuous roll and is dipped in and out of the dye by means of the cylinder of steel slats seen inside the machine.

Below: a continuous wet steam dyeing process. The fabric is first impregnated with finely distributed dye in water. In the steamer the reduction and solution of the dye takes place. At this stage it looks blue but after oxidation the dye regains its permanent yellow colour.

with the cotton dyes. Acetate fibre (a product of acetic acid and cellulose), however, provided difficulties and the *disperse dyes* were developed in the 1920s for this fibre. They are water-insoluble azo and anthracene dyes that dissolve in acetate at elevated temperatures. They are prepared as very fine aqueous dispersions stabilized by colloids such as soap and glue. At 80 to 85 °C (176 to 185 °F), the dispersed dye penetrates into the fibre, where it is firmly held.

Disperse dyes are also used for the newest synthetic fibre, the polyesters. Polyamides can also be dyed with disperse dyes, but normally acid dyes are used. Acrylics are practically always dyed with basic dyes, which often are also azo dyes.

All the dyes are applied to textiles as aqueous solutions or dispersions, but the expense and shortage of water and the problems associated with effluent disposal have led to attempts to use organic solvents (white spirit, benzene, hydrocarbons). These have met with little success so far.

Dyeing methods

The process of dyeing is dynamic. Since the dye must have an affinity for the fibre, it will tend to migrate from the solution on to the fibre, and it is essential that this migration should be quite uniform. To achieve this, either the material or the dye liquor must be kept moving to ensure a regular flow through the material. Spent liquor must be returned from the surface of the fibre for intimate remixing with the main body of the liquor to promote a steady fall in dye concentration in the bath.

The textile material may be dyed as loose fibre, yarn, or woven or knitted fabric, the form depending on subsequent processing. For instance, previously dyed yarn is required for producing multicoloured fabrics. The various forms are dyed in appropriate machines. Loose fibres are compressed into per-

BASF

forated containers and the dye liquor is pumped through. Yarns are wound on to perforated tubes through which the liquor passes into the body of the yarn package. Woven fabrics can also be dyed in this way on perforated beams but there is usually one big difference in that the material does not remain at rest but rotates rapidly to keep the liquor in turbulent motion, thus ensuring evenness of dyeing. This is necessary because any irregularities in the dyeing become apparent at once on a fabric.

All dyeing machines are heated because the affinity between dye and material increases with temperature. With polyester fibres, maximum affinity exists at well above the boiling point of water (100°C) and a pressurized dyeing vessel is therefore needed because higher temperatures are attainable only when the pressure is increased to a few atmospheres.

In *pigment dyeing*, affinity between dye and fibre is of no consequence. Organic or inorganic water-insoluble colourants of the type used in paints and lacquers are prepared in the form of fine aqueous suspensions. A water-soluble resin that becomes insoluble on heating is added. After impregnation with pigment and resin, the material is dried and brought rapidly to a temperature of around 120°C (248°F). The now insoluble resin adheres firmly to the fibre and retains the pigment at the same time. Although the fibres are coloured only on the surface, the method is useful for many purposes.

FABRIC PRINTING is a form of dyeing in which only certain parts of a fabric are coloured, or a variety of colours are brought on to the fabric alongside one another. The dyes are those used in dyeing, but the relatively concentrated solutions are made into pastes by adding thickening agents (starch pastes, alginates, and so on). These can be printed by means of screen stencils or engraved metal rollers. Naturally, a separate screen or roller is required for each colour. After printing, the cloth is dried and then steamed to induce diffusion of the dyes into the fibre. Finally the water-soluble thickener is washed out.

Dye fastness

Nowadays, dyed and printed textiles are expected to have *fastness properties* that were previously unattainable. There is quite a range of these properties (fastness to perspiration, acids, ironing, and so on), the consumer being mainly concerned with light- and wash-fastness. The latter is quickly determined by giving a wash test under defined conditions.

Testing for light-fastness is not as simple, especially during the winter months, and equipment for exposing the test specimens to intense radiations similar to those of sunlight had been developed. The test dyeings are exposed to this irradiation together with a standard dyeing of known light-fastness as a control. The specimens are checked for changes in shade at regular intervals. With this method, the light-fastness of a dye or dyeing can be established within hours as against the several weeks, or even months, needed with daylight testing.

Light-fastness is divided into eight grades, 8 being the highest. A rating of 8 means that a dyeing will retain its shade until the material is worn out and has served its purpose. Nowadays there are very many high-quality dyes with this rating, for example, among the vat dyes which also have the highest ratings for other fastness properties. The dye chemist is constantly endeavouring to produce dyes that have maximum fastness ratings on all natural and man-made fibres.

Above: a high temperature beam dyeing machine. The material, which is wound on a perforated roller, remains stationary while the dyeing liquor is pumped through. Here the fabric is driven out of the container after completion of the dyeing.

Left: polyester yarn wound on perforated tubes. The whole assembly is being lifted from the dyeing machine. During the dyeing process the dyestuff is pumped through the holes in the tube.

DYNAMICS

Dynamics is a branch of physics concerned with moving bodies
—their direction, speed, momentum and energy, and the inter-
relation of these quantities. It therefore represents one side of
the subject of mechanics, the other being STATICS—the study of
stationary bodies, and the forces on these, in a stable, non-
moving, situation. The design of a bridge, for example, requires
the use of statics to determine its structural stability. Dynamics,
on the other hand, being concerned with movement, seeks to
determine quantitatively the effects of a force on a body's
motion and as such is closely related to the subject of applied
mathematics. Indeed, once the relevant laws of physics have
been employed to analyze the given situation and establish the
mathematical expressions of these laws, the problem becomes
largely one of the manipulation and solution of equations.

Kinematics and kinetics

Dynamics is split into two
subsections: kinematics and kinetics. *Kinematics* deals with the
mathematical description of the body's motion such as its
speed and velocity, and does not actually touch the physics of
the situation. Once this is done, an analysis from the point of
view of the laws of physics that govern motion is performed:
this is the *kinetics* part of the investigation.

*Below: some concepts in dynamics. In (A) a mass M is shown—this
is a scalar quantity because it has no direction. In (B), the two cars
have the same (scalar) speed but different (vector) velocities because
they move in different directions. The bow in (C) converts potential
(stored) energy into kinetic (motive) energy. A (vector) force on a
mass produces an acceleration—this is also a vector quantity (shown
in D). In rotary motion (E) torque produces angular acceleration.*

History

Sir Isaac NEWTON'S LAWS of motion formulated in
the seventeenth century and developed by later physicists and
mathematicians were spectacularly successful in their explana-
tions and analysis of many problems, from the motion of planets
around the sun to the behaviour of tiny particles of dust. The
discovery of Neptune in the mid-nineteenth century, for
example, was not due to improvements in the optical properties of telescopes, but to the application of dynamics.

A dynamical analysis of the solar system had shown that the
observed motions of the known planets were at variance with
what was predicted theoretically. It was then realized that the
existence of an eighth planet was necessary as the deviations
could only be explained if there was a distant planet whose
gravitational attraction was distorting the orbits of the others.
The analysis even predicted where to look for this planet, its
size and some details of its orbit around the sun. It was located
within a couple of degrees of the calculated position by
Professor Galle in Berlin in 1846, following independent
calculations by Leverrier in France and Adams in England.

Scalar and vector quantities

In dynamics there is
found first a precise definition of all the properties that bodies
exhibit because they are moving—these properties are called
dynamical variables and include speed, velocity, acceleration,
momentum and energy.

Speed is defined as distance travelled per unit time and is a
scalar quantity, meaning that it has a magnitude expressed only in
units of speed such as miles per hour or metres per second.
Many dynamical variables, however, are *vector quantities* which
means that they must be assigned a direction in space as well
as a magnitude.

OSBORNE/MARKS

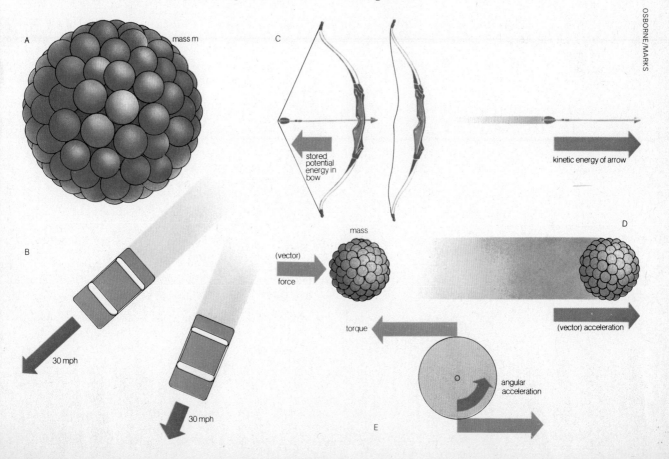

A   mass m

C   stored potential energy in bow   kinetic energy of arrow

B   30 mph   30 mph

mass   (vector) force   (vector) acceleration   D

torque   angular acceleration

E

Velocity, for example, is defined as speed in a particular direction and is a vector quantity. Thus two cars may have the same speed if they cover the same distance in the same time, but will only have the same velocity if they are travelling in the same direction (that is, parallel). Momentum is also a vector quantity because it is defined as mass multiplied by velocity and the direction of this vector is the same as the velocity vector involved in its calculation.

The momentum of a body is a measure of how difficult it is to bring it to rest. Consider two bodies, one with twice the mass of the other but the smaller mass travelling with twice the speed of the larger. They are equally difficult to stop because the doubled mass of the slower body compensates for the higher speed of the smaller mass—each body has the same momentum.

Vectors are of fundamental importance because a body will only change its line of travel, or more generally, its momentum, if it is forced to do so. Just how large that force must be and exactly how quickly (and by how much) it will alter its direction is basically what dynamics is all about.

The concept of force is central to the whole theory of dynamics. Newton's laws of motion state that a body's momentum (and therefore its speed and direction of travel) can only be changed by the application of a force. The rate of change of momentum with time is determined by the magnitude of the force and the direction of change by the direction in which the force acts. Force is therefore also a vector quantity.

Energy, work and power

When a body is moving, it possesses energy, and this is called *kinetic energy*. This may be harnessed and put to a useful purpose. Hydroelectric power stations do just that with the energy of moving water. The water passes through turbines which 'tap' the kinetic energy of the river and turn this into electrical energy. In the process, the water is slowed down, that is, it yields part of its energy associated with its motion. To slow down a car the brakes are applied. This converts some of the kinetic energy of the moving vehicle into heat, which is dissipated by the brakes, thus slowing it down.

Another form of energy is *potential energy*. This is the energy that a body possesses by virtue of its position in a force field. For example, a body held above the ground has the 'potential' to fall to the ground in the Earth's gravitational field. While falling it loses its potential energy but gains in speed and therefore gains kinetic energy. On reaching the ground it has no potential energy left—it no longer has any 'potential' to move. An arrow acquires potential energy when it is drawn back in a bow by virtue of the tension (force) in the string. When it is released, all this potential energy is transferred to kinetic energy.

Both potential and kinetic energy are forms of *stored energy*—one is stored by virtue of its position, the other by virtue of its motion. *Work*, on the other hand, is the amount of energy *transferred* to a body. It is, for example, the amount of energy imparted to a body when a force acts on it. *Power* is another important dynamical variable as it is the *rate* at which energy is transferred in time, that is, the rate of doing work. Energy, work and power are all scalar quantities because they cannot be related to a specific direction. Energy, for example, can be harnessed to do work in any direction.

Rotary motion

With linear motion the force acting on a body is equal to the mass of the body times its acceleration (Newton's laws). With a rotating body there is a similar relationship between the twisting force, or *torque* (from the Latin verb 'torquere'—to twist), and angular acceleration; torque is equal to the moment of INERTIA of the body (inertia is resistance to being moved) times the angular acceleration.

Dynamics and modern physics

Like so many branches of physics, dynamics had to be substantially revised in the light of modern discoveries. To explain properly the newly observed phenomena that occur on the microscopic level, such as the collisions and interactions between electrons and nuclei, Newtonian (or as it is now known, classical) mechanics is inadequate and QUANTUM mechanics is required. Also, the strange behaviour of bodies moving with speeds comparable to that of light cannot be explained by classical mechanics and relativistic mechanics becomes important. Practical applications on the scale and complexity of those found in most real-life engineering projects, however, need not resort to such advanced approaches.

CAMERA PRESS

Left: dynamics is the science of moving bodies and the forces which produce and affect motion. The flight path of a rocket, for example, is determined by the thrust of the motors, the earth's gravitational pull, the latitude of the launch site and air currents. These factors are fed into a computer to determine speed and position.

DYNAMO

A dynamo is a rotating machine which converts mechanical energy into electrical energy. The term 'dynamo' was originally used to cover both alternating current (AC) generators, or ALTERNATORS, and direct current (DC) generators, but nowadays it usually refers to the DC type only.

Basic principles
The dynamo, like the alternator, makes use of a phenomenon discovered by Michael FARADAY (1791–1867). In general terms, when an electrical conductor is moved in the vicinity of a magnet, a voltage is created, or *induced*, in the conductor. If the ends of the conductor are connected in any kind of closed electrical CIRCUIT, this induced voltage (electrical pressure) causes a current to flow in the circuit. Mechanical energy has been converted into electrical energy.

For a more detailed explanation it is necessary to consider the principles of ELECTROMAGNETISM. In an electrical circuit it is voltage that causes the current to flow. The voltage, or *electromotive force* (emf) is the cause and current the effect. By analogy, in a magnetic circuit the driving 'pressure' is called the *magnetomotive force* (mmf). This is the cause and *magnetic flux* is the result, or effect. Between the north and south poles of a magnet in the medium surrounding the magnet can be envisaged a set of *flux lines*—the closer these lines are together the greater the *flux density*. Flux density is determined by the mmf of the magnet and the *permeability* of the surrounding medium (see MAGNETISM).

The emf induced in an electrical conductor, moving in a magnetic field, is determined by the rate at which the conductor 'cuts' the lines of flux. The induced emf is therefore related to the speed of the conductor and the flux density. It is also related to the length of the conductor.

A simple alternator
When a closed rectangular loop of wire is mounted on a rotating axis (the rotor) and rotated between the north and south poles of a horseshoe magnet (the stator), the following occurs. When the two sides of the loop parallel to the axis of the rotor (these are the 'conductors') form a line between the north and south poles, the rate at which these two conductors cut the lines of flux is at a maximum. The induced emf in the conductors is therefore also at a maximum and the current flowing around the loop at its largest value.

When the rotor has turned through 90°, the instantaneous direction of motion of the conductors is along the lines of flux. No lines of flux are therefore cut, no emf is induced in them and the loop current is zero.

When it has rotated by a further 90°, the rate of flux cutting is again a maximum with maximum emf and loop current. The loop is now, however, 'upside down' compared to its position 180° ago and the induced emf and current are a maximum in the opposite direction. A further 90° rotation and the current is again zero.

By breaking the loop at one end near the axis and connecting

Below: a cutaway drawing of the kind of dynamo that is used in a car. The dynamo is usually bolted to the engine and driven by the fan belt which passes over the pulley at the end. The fins on the back of the drive pulley act as a cooling fan, blowing air through the dynamo to cool the windings which would otherwise become very hot because of the current flowing through them.

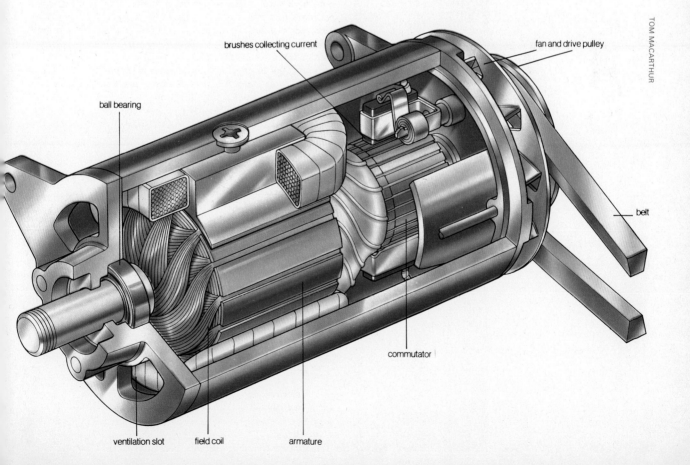

TOM MACARTHUR

brushes collecting current

fan and drive pulley

ball bearing

belt

ventilation slot   field coil   armature   commutator

the ends to two slip rings on the shaft of the rotor, this alternating emf can be tapped using 'brushes' touching the rings to drive an external electrical circuit. This is the basic design of an alternator.

From alternators to dynamos

To construct a dynamo, several loops are positioned in sequence around the rotor. This time, instead of taking the loop ends to slip rings, they are connected in the same sequence to individual segments of a commutator (a divided rotating contact). Two brushes are mounted on opposite sides of the commutator such that, as the rotor rotates, the brushes form an electrical contact with the two ends of just one loop at a time.

By positioning the brushes so that they 'tap' that loop which is in the position of maximum flux cutting, then they will tap each loop as it comes into that position during rotation. The induced emf is therefore always in the same direction (that is, a DC voltage) and always with the maximum value possible. This is the simple dynamo.

Increasing the speed of rotation will, to a certain extent, increase the DC voltage available at the brushes. One other way to improve the dynamo performance is to increase the number of turns in each 'loop'—thus making a coil—because, as already stated, the length of the conductor also determines the emf that can be induced. Finally, the performance can be further improved by increasing the flux density. Several methods are available for this. First, stronger magnets or electromagnets can be employed and, second, the magnetic poles pieces can be shaped to concentrate the lines of flux.

When electromagnets are used to provide the magnetic field they draw some of the current generated by the machine. When starting from rest, the current to start the electromagnets working is derived from what little residual magnetism exists in the electromagnets and surrounding magnetic circuit.

Below: this 3350 kW, 660 volt DC generator or dynamo operates at 53 rpm. The principle of the generator is that a wire moving through a magnetic field has a voltage induced in it. Here, the rotor consists of a set of wire coils mounted on a rotating shaft and connected to a commutator. The stator contains electromagnets.